RESIDENTIAL CONCRETE

by NAHB Research Foundation, Inc.

National Association of Home Builders
15th and M Streets, N.W.
Washington, D.C. 20005

Contents

Preface iv

Part 1. Understanding Concrete

Concrete Basics 1
  Hydration and Water 1
    Problems from Too Much Water 2
  Hydration and Curing 2

Mix Design 3

Slump 4

Air Entrainment 4
  Air-Entrainment Formula Variations
  and Precautions 4

Admixtures 5
  Accelerators 5
    Calcium Chloride 5
    Other Accelerators 5
    Accelerating Concrete Without
    Admixtures 5
  Retarders 5
    Another Method of Concrete Retardation 6
  Plasticizers or Water Reducers 6
  Superplasticizers or High-Range
  Water Reducers 6
    Guidelines for Using Superplasticizers 6

Finishing 7

Uniformity 7

Concreting in Extreme Weather 7
  Hot, Dry, or Windy Weather 7
  Cold Weather 7
    Resisting Freeze-Thaw and Deicers 7

Controlling Cracking 7
  Poor or Nonexistent Jointing
  Causes Cracking 8
  Controlling Cracking with Good Jointing 8
  Wire Mesh 9
  Reinforcing Steel 9
  Special Cement 9

Synopsis of Basic Requirements 9

Part 2. Concrete Practices

Formbuilding 11
  Footings 11
    Metal Stakes and Spreaders 12
    Combined Low Wall and Footing
    (Monolithic) 12
    Stepped Footing 13
    Corner Fastening 13
  Forming Curbs and Gutters 14
  Forming a Slab on Grade 15
  Forming a Curved Slab or Curb 15
  Forming Walls 16

Reusable Job-Built Plywood
  Form Panels 17
  Forming Door and Window Openings 18
  Single-Wall Forming 19
Forming Stairs 20
  Typical Low Exterior Stairs 20
  Riser Bracing for Wide Stairs 21
  Fastening Riser Form to Concrete
  or Masonry Wall 22
  Stair Support 22
  Open Stairs 23

Jointing 24
  Control Joints 24
    Locating Control Joints 24
    Control Joints for Topping Slabs 25
    Control Joints for Curbs 26
    Cutting Control Joints 26
    Sealing Control Joints 26
    Structural Slabs and Control Joints 26
    Basement Slabs and Control Joints 27
  Isolation Joints 27
    An Alternate Way to Form Isolation
    Joints 28
    Other Examples of Isolation Joint
    Locations 28
  Construction Joints 29

Making Concrete Watertight 29
  Special Waterproofing Measures 30
  Waterproofing a Slab 31
  Waterproofing Wall Joints 31

Layout Guidelines for Concrete Slabs 32
  Recommended Slopes 32
    Driveways, Patios, Sidewalks 32
    Basement Slab 32
  Recommended Thicknesses 33
  Setting the Grade 33
    Using Transit or Builder's Level 33
    Using a Story Pole 33
    Dots and Wet Screeds 34

Preparing the Subgrade 35
  Fill 35
  Dampening 35
  The Subgrade in Hot Weather 35
  The Subgrade in Cold Weather 36
  Earth Collapse 36

Installing Reinforcement 36
  Wire Mesh 36
    Where to Place Mesh 36
    Control Joints and Mesh 36
    Ductwork and Mesh 36
    Size of Mesh 36
  Reinforcing Steel 37
    Cover for Reinforcing Steel 37
    Lapping Reinforcing Steel 37

The Concrete 37

Placing the Concrete....................... 39
   Placing Concrete for Steps 39
   Cement Contact—Caution 39

Finishing the Concrete 39
   Striking Off and Bullfloating 40
   Edging 40
      Avoiding a High or Dished Edge........... 40
   Making Control Joints 41
      Hand-tooling the Joint.................. 41
      Sawing the Joint...................... 41
      Sealing Control Joints 42
   Floating and Troweling 42
      When to Start ...., 42
      Hand Floating and Troweling........... 42
      Power Floating and Troweling 42
   Finishing Stairs 43
      Early Stripping Method 43
      Late Stripping Method 43
   Grout Cleandown, Sacking, and
   Rubbing 43
   Placing and Finishing in Hot, Dry, or
   Windy Weather 44
   Placing and Finishing in Cold Weather 44

Curing.................................. 44
   Curing Without Adding Water 45
      Polyethylene Cure 45
      Waterproof Paper 46
      Liquid-Membrane-Curing Compounds....... 46
   Curing by Adding Water 48
      Wet Burlap.......................... 48
      Sprinkling or Fogging.................. 48
      Ponding 48
   Curing in Hot, Dry, or Windy Weather 50
   Curing in Cold Weather 50

Part 3. Concrete Problems

Crazing, Dusting, Scaling 51

Spalling 52

Scaling and Spalling, Freeze-Thaw,
and Deicers.............................. 53

Cracks 53
   Plastic-Shrinkage Cracks 54

Blisters 54

Bugholes 55

Pitting 55

Popouts 55

Curling 55

Blowups 55

Efflorescence 55

Discoloration.............................. 56

Flash Set 56

Cold Joint 56

Dished Surface or High Edges 56

Patching and Repairing....................... 57
   Patching Spalled Areas with Concrete 57
   Patching Spalled Areas with Epoxy 58
      Making an Epoxy-Mortar Patch............. 58
      Additional Uses for Epoxy 59
   Patching Spalled Areas with Latex
   Mortar.............................. 59
   Other Patching Agents 59
   Resurfacing Slabs ....,,..... 59
      Applying a Bonded Topping................ 59
      Applying an Unbonded Topping 60
   Correcting Pinholes and Projections 60
   Patching Tieholes 60
   Repairing a Broken Corner 61
   Repairing Honeycomb...................... 61

Part 4. Special Finishes

Colored Concrete........................... 63
   Four Ways to Color a Slab 63
   Making Good Colored Concrete 63

White Concrete............................. 64
   Mixing, Handling, and Finishing 64

Dry-Shake Technique 64
   Applying Dry Shakes 64
   Hardness and Wear and Slip Resistance 64

Exposed-Aggregate Finish by Seeding 65

Nonslip Finishes 66
   Floated Swirl 66
   Burlap Drag........................... 66
   Wire Combing 66
   Broom Finish.......................... 67

Other Special Finishes 67
   Rock-Salt Texture 67
   Travertine Finish........................ 67
   Flagstone Pattern 68
   Flagstone Pattern—Alternative Method 69
   Other Designs......................... 69

**Appendix. Model Ordinance to Reduce
Scaling and Spalling**....................... 70

The NAHB Research Foundation, Inc., is a wholly owned subsidiary of the National Association of Home Builders that carries out NAHB-sponsored research programs. It also performs research and development for private manufacturers of building materials and equipment and for departments and agencies of the Federal Government.

NAHB ISBN 0-86718-158-3

Library of Congress Catalog Card Number: 83-60008

12/89 Reproductions 750
5/91 Reproductions 1500

Preface

Residential Concrete covers just about all the home builder needs to know about good quality concreting. While not a training manual, it provides enough information on technique to allow the builder to recognize most faulty practices.

Guidelines are given for ordering ready mixed concrete. Admixtures such as accelerators, retarders, plasticizers, and superplasticizers are discussed. Sections on formbuilding, jointing, and basement leakage control are illustrated.

Curing is given special attention since it is often done poorly. Proper curing may double the strength of concrete as well as greatly increase watertightness. All the basic cures are discussed, including their advantages and disadvantages.

A comprehensive section is devoted to concrete problems and remedies. In fact, the problems of scaling and spalling were the main reason the National Association of Home Builders' Standing Committee on Research commissioned this manual. Plastic-shrinkage cracks, blisters, and popouts are among the problems covered. Patching techniques with latex, epoxy, and dry-mix concrete are given. Throughout the manual special measures for cold weather and for hot, dry, windy weather are discussed. The detailed list of contents enables the reader to turn directly to any topic.

The author and illustrator of *Residential Concrete* is Laurence Miller of the NAHB Research Foundation, Inc., under the guidance of Lee Fisher, Director of Industrial Engineering, and Ralph J. Johnson, Director and President of the Foundation. The Technical Services Department of the National Association of Home Builders aided in review of the manual, as did builder members of the Standing Committee on Research. However, their advice and assistance in no way imply an endorsement.

Concrete Basics
Hydration and Water

Cement particles, through the process of hydration, develop long crystals when wet, and these crystals bond the concrete mix together.

As long as moisture is present and the temperature is not too low, the crystals can continue to grow for years and increase the strength of the concrete. Cement needs only a small amount of water to hydrate. Too much water will seriously weaken the concrete.

The water-to-cement ratio is important. Typically, the ratio should be 0.50 or less by weight—or no more than ½ pound of water to 1 pound of cement. The water already in the sand must always be included when measuring the water. The 0.50 ratio is necessary for durability, watertightness, and strength. If the concrete is difficult to work, a plasticizer may be used.

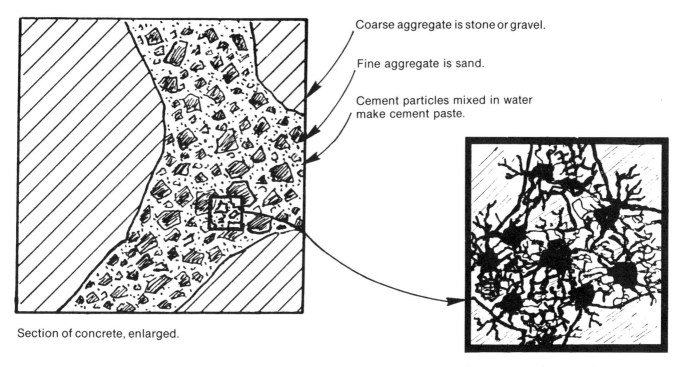

Coarse aggregate is stone or gravel.

Fine aggregate is sand.

Cement particles mixed in water make cement paste.

Section of concrete, enlarged.

Cement crystals grow close together in properly mixed concrete.

When too much water is used, the cement crystals are far apart and the concrete is much weaker.

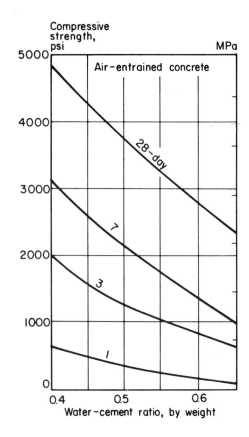

A water-to-cement ratio that is too high cuts concrete strength and greatly affects watertightness.

Problems from Too Much Water

Too much water in the mix can create water reservoirs in the concrete and cause it to bleed. Channels lead from the reservoirs to the surface where a watery laitance forms and a weak surface results. The concrete may craze, dust, and scale, especially if finishing operations are done while bleed water is still present. If the water reservoirs and channels dry out, air pockets will remain and allow water and deicers to enter. Should the water freeze and expand, it will harm the concrete. Deicers also seriously harm non-air-entrained concrete.

Air-entrainment lessens bleeding and helps protect the concrete against freeze and thaw and deicers. However, even entrained air loses some of its effectiveness in a soupy mix.

Hydration and Curing

As long as concrete is allowed to cure, it continues to gain strength and watertightness, even for years after it is placed. The greatest gain, however, is in the first week or two after placing—and it is then that curing is most important.

Uncured concrete dries out and may reach only half its design strength.

In addition to increasing concrete's strength, curing also reduces its shrinkage stress. A combination of increased strength and stress reduction means fewer cracks.

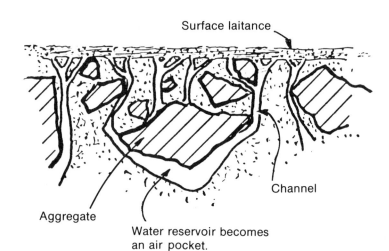

Surface laitance

Channel

Aggregate

Water reservoir becomes an air pocket.

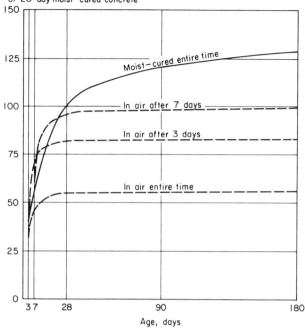

Concrete strength increases with age as long as moisture and favorable temperatures are present. Good curing more than doubles the strength of concrete.

Subgrade should be properly moistened before placing concrete so that too much water from the mix does not go into the subgrade. A good cure will retain water in the concrete.

A low water-cement ratio and good curing combined can more than triple—even quadruple—the strength of concrete and increase its watertightness and its resistance to spalling and cracking.

Mix Design

The right proportions of all ingredients, not just the water-to-cement ratio, must be maintained; for example:
- Too much cement paste in relation to aggregate is not only costly, but will produce concrete that is not durable and will crack easily.
- Too much aggregate (sand and stone) makes the mix stiff and difficult to place and finish. Too much fine aggregate (sand) requires excess water and may cause the concrete to crack. Too much coarse aggregate (stone) produces a porous and honeycombed concrete.

For guidelines on specifying ready mixed concrete, see "The Concrete," page 37.

Slump

Slump is a measure of the consistency or stiffness of fresh concrete. It is influenced by the amount of water—more water means higher slump—but water is not the only influence. The type of aggregate, the air content, and the proportions of all the ingredients affect slump.

The slump test, illustrated here, is a measure of the workability of concrete when wet and also a check of the concrete's consistency from batch to batch.

Typical slumps for various jobs are given in the mix design table on **page 37**.

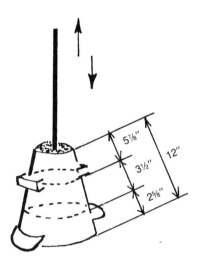

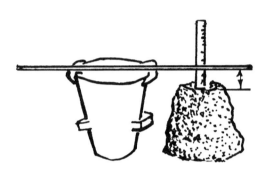

Slump test. Step 1. Fill the cone in three layers of equal volume, rodding each layer 25 times.

Step 2. Strike off the top, then remove the cone slowly with an even motion, taking from 5 to 10 seconds. Do not jar the mixture or tilt the cone in the process.

Step 3. Measure the slump with tamping rod and ruler. The slump test should not take longer than 1½ minutes. Do not use the same batch of concrete for any other test.

Air Entrainment

Air entrainment is essential for protecting concrete exposed to freezing and thawing and deicers.

An air-entraining admixture or air-entraining cement causes microscopic air bubbles to form throughout the concrete where they act as relief valves when the concrete freezes, helping to prevent scaling or spalling of the surface. Resistance to deicers, which also cause scaling and spalling, is greater if the air-entrained concrete is air-dried for about four weeks after curing.

Air-entrained concrete is more watertight; more resistant to sulfate soils; and easier to work—provided the right tools are used—particularly if the mixture is lean or has angular aggregates. Concrete strength is reduced somewhat by air entrainment, but a lower water-cement ratio is possible in an air-entrained mix and this makes up for any lost strength.

Magnesium or aluminum tools should be used to bull-float and finish air-entrained concrete mixtures, because wood floats tend to tear the surface of this type of mixture.

Table 1. Recommended Air Content for Concrete Subject to Severe Exposure Conditions, by Aggregate Size*

Maximum-size coarse aggregate in inches	Air content, percent by volume of concrete**
1½, 2, or 2½	5 ± 1
¾ or 1	6 ± 1
⅜ or ½	7½ ± 1

*See text for formula variations and precautions.
**Air content in mortar alone should be about 9 percent.

Air Entrainment Formula Variations and Precautions

- Add 2 percent to the values shown in Table 1 for structural-lightweight-aggregate concrete.

4

- Some entrained air tends to be lost in hot weather, so the percentage of air should be slightly higher.
- Some admixtures, such as certain water-reducers, retarders, and superplasticizers affect air entrainment and have to be taken into consideration when determining the amount of air-entraining agent needed.
- In very-low-slump concrete, the proper amount of air entrainment is hard to attain without using a water-reducing admixture.
- Soupy or watery mixtures tend to lose entrained air rapidly.
- Admixtures to reduce excess air entrainment are available from suppliers.

Concrete that is not air entrained may be used for basement slabs or wherever concrete is not exposed to freezing and thawing or deicers; but since air-entrained concrete helps control bleeding and segregation and is easy to work, it may be preferred. If concrete without air entrainment is used, wooden bullfloats and hand floats are recommended.

Admixtures

All admixtures used should meet American Society for Testing and Materials (ASTM) Designation: C494 standards.

Accelerators

Accelerators speed up the setting time and strength development of concrete and are especially useful in cold weather. They can be combined with water-reducing admixtures. Always check manufacturers' recommendations before using an accelerator.

Calcium Chloride

Calcium chloride is the most commonly used accelerator. It is not an antifreeze, but it speeds up the set and makes freezing damage less likely, especially if the concrete is insulated. Precautions to take when using calcium chloride include—

- Add it in liquid form as part of the mixing water. If calcium chloride is added in dry form, it may not dissolve completely and can cause popouts and dark spots in the concrete as well as affect the air-entraining admixture.
- Never add more than 2 percent of calcium chloride by weight of cement. A greater amount causes the concrete to stiffen rapidly and makes placing and finishing difficult. Too much calcium chloride may also cause flash set, increase shrinkage (a cause of cracking), corrode reinforcement, and weaken and discolor the concrete.
- Do not use calcium chloride when the concrete is to contain embedded aluminum such as conduit.

Serious corrosion can result, especially if the aluminum is near or in contact with steel and the weather is humid.
- Do not use calcium chloride if galvanized steel is to be permanently in contact with the concrete.
- Do not use calcium chloride if the concrete is to be exposed to soil or water that contains sulfates or is subject to alkali-aggregate reaction.
- Do not use polyethylene film for curing a concrete that contains calcium chloride because the concrete will become discolored.
- Some aggregates may not be compatible with calcium chloride. The concrete supplier should be checked when there is any question at all about an aggregate.

Other Accelerators

Before trying accelerators other than calcium chloride, independent evaluations should be obtained.

Accelerating Concrete Without Admixtures

Since calcium chloride requires such care and may increase drying shrinkage, the following alternative methods should be considered:

Type III, High-Early-Strength, Portland Cement. Type III portland cement gains strength almost twice as fast as Type I, normal, cement on the first day the concrete mixture is placed. However, the strengths are more or less equal after about three months.

Lower Water-Cement Ratio. A lower water-cement ratio accelerates strength gain, but too much cement is costly and may cause cracking in the concrete.

Curing at Higher Temperature. Higher temperatures speed up strength gain considerably.

Heated Mixing Water. Warming the mix by using heated water can accelerate strength gain.

Retarders

Retarders are useful in hot weather when the concrete may set so quickly that it cannot be finished properly. Retarders are also useful when difficult placements require more time. Retarders that are also water reducers or plasticizers, called water-reducing retarders, slow down the set while speeding up placement by plasticizing the concrete. Not all plasticizers retard the set. Precautions to take when using retarders:
- Retarders may entrain some air into the concrete. Check on the extent and allow for it when figuring amount of air-entraining agent.
- Some strength reduction usually occurs during the first one to three days when retarders are used.
- Other effects of retarders may vary with the product, so manufacturers' recommendations must be checked before using.

- A mixture may be accidentally retarded by even a slight amount of sugar in it. Such contamination can result in strength reduction and even failure.

Another Method of Concrete Retardation

In hot weather concrete sets more slowly when the aggregate or water, or both, are cooled. One very effective method is to use chipped ice for part of the mixing water.

Plasticizers or Water Reducers

Plasticizers make the concrete more workable with less water. Thus, concrete strength is increased by the low water-cement ratio and labor costs are reduced since the concrete is more workable.

Some water reducers may increase drying shrinkage, and this may increase cracking. Other water reducers, however, will reduce shrinkage cracks, according to the manufacturers.

Water reducers may also be accelerators or retarders. The type chosen should fit the circumstance. For example, an accelerating water reducer is suitable for cold weather; a retarding water reducer is suitable for hot weather.

Some water reducers also entrain air. Allow for the extent of this entrainment when specifying amounts of air-entraining agent.

Water-reducers are worth investigating if the concrete needs added strength without increasing labor costs.

Superplasticizers or High-Range Water Reducers

An ordinary water reducer can reduce water 10 to 15 percent while slightly increasing slump. A superplasticizer can increase slump dramatically from an original 3 inches to 7 or 8 inches. Since concrete mixtures with superplasticizers are much easier to place, labor costs can be reduced.

A superplasticized concrete mix is easier to work not only because of the almost liquid slump, but also because of the consistency of the concrete. Cement masons liken it to a temporary lubrication of the mix. It can be chuted easier at a lower angle and is almost self-leveling.

The slump increase lasts about 30 to 60 minutes, and then the mix returns to its original low-slump condition. However, if a conventional water-reducing retarder is used with a reduced amount of superplasticizer, the high slump lasts as long as 2 or 3 hours.

If slump is lost too soon, more superplasticizer or more water may be added to retain slump. More water, however, weakens the concrete. The return of slump to normal after a short time is not the same as the concrete setting up. Whether or not the superplasticizer affects the set depends on the type and amount used. Typically, the set of high-strength concrete is retarded when a small amount of superplasticizer is used, particularly if a conventional water-reducing retarder is used along

with it. But if more superplasticizer is used, the set may be accelerated.

Segregation of the large aggregate is usually not a problem with superplasticized mixes as it often is with conventional high-slump mixes. Superplasticized mixes with extremely high slumps, however, may have some segregation.

Superplasticizers do affect air entrainment, although authorities disagree at present on how much. This effect in turn may or may not affect resistance to freezing and thawing or deicers. In any case an air-entraining admixture should be added just before placing the superplasticized concrete mix.

Costs for superplasticizers range from about $3.00 to $3.25 in 1981 dollars per cubic yard of concrete. However, the net concreting cost may be less because the cement content of the mix may be reduced and labor costs may be reduced for placing and finishing. Costs may be reduced even more by using a conventional water-reducing retarder along with a reduced amount of superplasticizer. These steps also take some time pressure off the finisher.

Guidelines for Using Superplasticizers

- Organize well and run a tight schedule. Before the mix arrives, have forms inspected, a cleared access for ready mix trucks, and a crew waiting.
- Use a conventional water-reducing retarder and less superplasticizer to allow more' working time and reduce cost. Add the water-reducer retarder before adding the superplasticizer.
- Add the air-entraining agent after adding the superplasticizer, if possible.
- Delay the final finishing until the concrete is firm enough to resist tearing. This delay may be longer than it would be for conventional concrete.
- If a ready mix truck is delayed and a superplasticized 8-inch-slump mix has to be placed against a reverted 3-inch-slump mix, blend the old and new concrete together.

Superplasticizers are relatively new in this country, although they have been used in Europe and Japan for some time. Since special attention should be given to the type of cement, aggregate, and admixture and to the overall mix proportions, users should work closely with reputable suppliers, check manufacturers' recommendations, and seek advice from organizations such as the following:

Concrete Construction Publications, Inc.
426 South Westgate
Addison, Illinois 60101

National Ready Mixed Concrete Association*
900 Spring Street
Silver Spring, Maryland 20910

---

*This group has a short helpful brochure called *Superplasticizers in Ready Mixed Concrete*, NRMCA Publication 158.

Portland Cement Association
5420 Old Orchard Road
Skokie, Illinois 60077

Finishing

Poor finishing can seriously impair the concrete surface. For good finishing, one of the most important skills is waiting. The mason must not do anything to the concrete while bleed water is on the surface.

When concrete is worked while bleed water is present, the sand, cement, and water at the surface are mixed together into a thin surface paste with a high water-cement ratio and a high sand content at the concrete's most vulnerable point. Crazing, dusting, and scaling or spalling are almost certain to result.

Good finishing done at the right time gives the concrete a hard dense surface, making it more durable and impermeable.

Uniformity

Whatever is done to concrete should be done uniformly and not suddenly. The following rules on uniformity should be strictly adhered to:

- Concrete should have about the same wetness all over when it is being cured, and the cure should be tapered off gradually. The subgrade should be uniformly damp when the concrete is placed.
- If the concrete is heated during curing, the heat should be uniformly distributed and tapered off gradually at the end of curing.
- The mix should be uniform from batch to batch and should not be worked so much that the aggregate is unevenly distributed.

Concreting in Extreme Weather*

Hot, Dry, or Windy Weather

Concrete sets up or hydrates much faster when the weather is warm. Since it loses moisture much faster in hot, dry, or windy weather, the following special measures are recommended:

- Plan ahead—have the subgrade prepared and workers and materials ready.
- Dampen the subgrade well in advance of placing; modify the mix as needed—adding more water and more cement, if needed, to maintain the same slump and water-cement ratio.
- Keep the mix cool; crushed ice for some of the mix water helps.
- Windbreaks, sunshades, wet covers, or fogging while working the concrete, as well as special curing techniques, may be needed.

- Admixtures to plasticize or retard the mix may also be helpful.

Cold Weather

Hydration slows down considerably in cold weather. Cold weather is a dangerous time for freshly poured concrete; for if the concrete freezes before it sets up, it will be less strong, durable, and watertight. Good curing reclaims some but not all of the desirable properties. Special cold-weather measures include the following:

- Make good preparations such as ordering heated concrete, using insulating materials, and preparing the subgrade so that it is not frozen when the concrete is laid.
- Use the right mix, including low slump and entrained air if the concrete is to be exposed to freeze-thaw or deicers.
- Use high-early-strength cement or accelerators such as calcium chloride, or both, for fast strength gain and be sure to follow recommendations.
- Heat or insulate the concrete, or both, if needed.
- Use special curing measures.

Resisting Freeze-Thaw and Deicers

Freeze-thaw cycles during cold weather may increase concrete's chances of scaling or spalling. Deicer salts can worsen the problem. Temperature changes also foster cracking.

Air entrainment has been mentioned as essential for concrete exposed to freeze-thaw or deicers. Other important measures are to control the water-cement ratio and slump, use the right curing technique, air-dry after curing, and apply special surface treatments.

Controlling Cracking

Concrete expands and contracts slightly with changes in its moisture content and temperature; and since it is low in tensile strength, it is apt to crack if it is restrained from moving as its volume changes. The problem is not to eliminate cracking, but rather to—

- Minimize cracking by using a minimum amount of water; using good curing techniques; preparing a good subgrade; isolating concrete sections if appropriate; and avoiding abrupt changes in temperature and moisture, particularly during curing.
- Control cracking by proper jointing or use of reinforcement, or both.

---

*Throughout this text the various topics give detailed techniques for extreme-weather concreting: admixtures, mixing, placing, finishing, curing, and so on.

Poor or nonexistent jointing causes cracking.

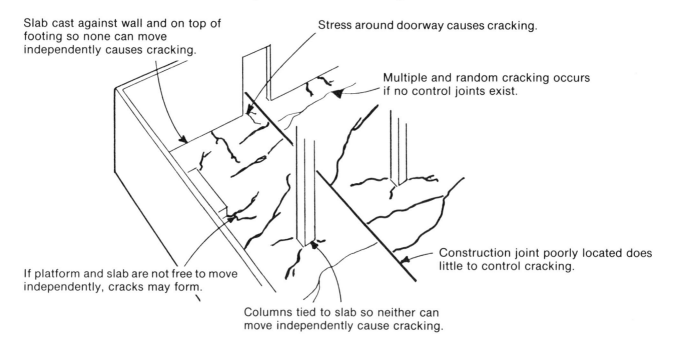

Slab cast against wall and on top of footing so none can move independently causes cracking.

Stress around doorway causes cracking.

Multiple and random cracking occurs if no control joints exist.

If platform and slab are not free to move independently, cracks may form.

Construction joint poorly located does little to control cracking.

Columns tied to slab so neither can move independently cause cracking.

Controlling Cracking with Good Jointing*

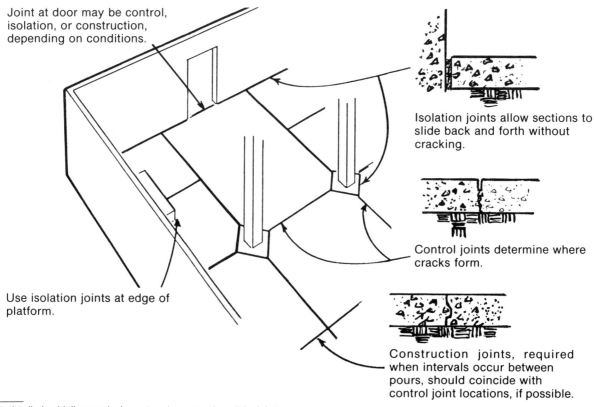

Joint at door may be control, isolation, or construction, depending on conditions.

Isolation joints allow sections to slide back and forth without cracking.

Control joints determine where cracks form.

Use isolation joints at edge of platform.

Construction joints, required when intervals occur between pours, should coincide with control joint locations, if possible.

*For detailed guidelines on laying out and constructing all the joints sketched, see "Jointing" and "Making Control Joints."

8

Wire Mesh

Mesh is often placed in slabs to control cracking. It distributes stresses so that many fine cracks develop rather than a few wide ones, and it helps hold the cracks tightly closed. The mesh keeps the aggregate interlocked and thus helps prevent displacement (the concrete on one side of a crack dropping lower than the other), which is important in exterior slabs such as sidewalks, patios, and drives.*

Debate continues about the value of mesh in slabs on grade; but since codes may require it anyway, the question is often how to use it best, rather than whether to use it.

Slab control joints can be spaced farther apart when mesh is used. The lap of the mesh should not coincide with a control joint.

Wire mesh should be located 2 inches down from the top of the slab to control surface shrinkage cracks.

Reinforcing Steel

Reinforcing steel (sometimes called rebars) typically is not used in footings or slabs on ground unless it is called for in the plans or specifications.

Steel might be used if ground support is not uniform. Two layers of the steel are required to prevent the concrete from sinking at one or more points. (See "Reinforcing Steel," page 37.)

Special Cement

Recently, shrinkage-compensating concretes made with expansive cement have been used to reduce cracking. The concrete actually expands as it cures, putting the steel under tension. For more information on this subject, check with suppliers or the Portland Cement Association.

Synopsis of Basic Requirements

To make concrete strong and hard, crack and spall resistant, weather durable, and waterproof:

- Start with a firm, uniform subgrade.
- Use a minimum amount of water in the mix. The water-cement ratio as a general rule should be not over 0.50 and the slump should be low. If necessary, use water reducers or superplasticizers to make low-slump concrete more workable.
- Use air entrainment for exterior or any other concrete exposed to freeze-thaw or deicers.
- Use a good mix design that will meet all of the job requirements.
- Place and work the concrete in a manner that avoids segregation of the mix.
- Finish the concrete correctly: Do not do anything when bleed water is present to avoid dusting, scaling, and crazing; make control joints one-quarter of the slab depth; make isolation joints where appropriate; float and trowel for a hard dense surface as appropriate.
- Use accelerators, retarders, and other admixtures wisely, since they may affect quality.
- Take special precautions in hot and cold weather.
- Cure the concrete properly; concrete's strength can be doubled by good curing.
- Plan ahead. Trying to remedy lack of planning by adding more water to concrete that is almost set will seriously affect the concrete's quality.

---

*The NAHB Home Owner's Warranty (HOW) Program allows a maximum displacement of ⅛ inch for a basement slab and ¼ inch for a garage slab.

Part 2. **CONCRETE PRACTICES**

Formbuilding

The basic rule for formbuilding is *think ahead*. Design the forms for the least cost overall by considering the reusability of materials and the labor both to build and disassemble them.

Footings

An excavated footing must have firm and uniform support. Therefore, an excavation that has been dug too deep or too wide should be left that way and the extra cut filled with concrete. This may be more economical than adding and compacting fill.

Excavated footing

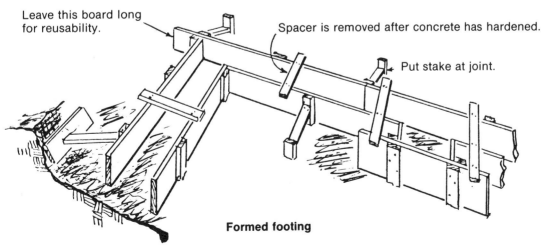

Leave this board long for reusability.

Spacer is removed after concrete has hardened.

Put stake at joint.

Formed footing

Metal Stakes and Spreaders

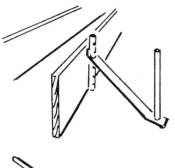
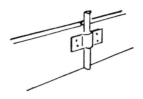
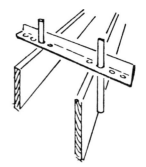

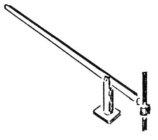

Metal stakes, braces, straps, and spreaders may save time and material, but without special stake pullers the advantage may be lost.

Combined Low Wall and Footing (Monolithic)

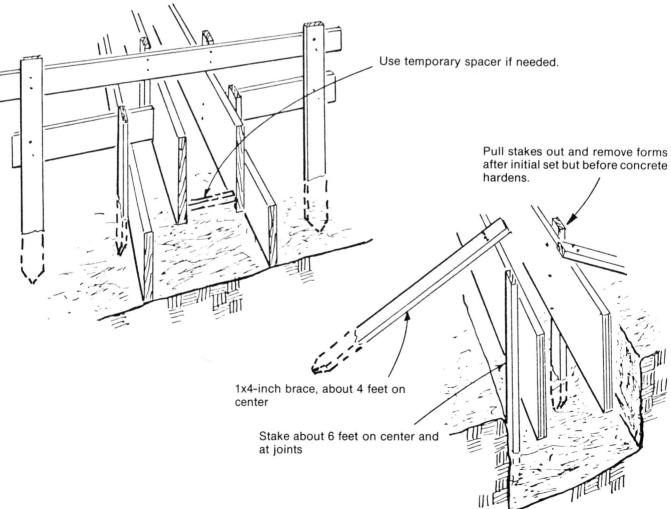

Use temporary spacer if needed.

Pull stakes out and remove forms after initial set but before concrete hardens.

1x4-inch brace, about 4 feet on center

Stake about 6 feet on center and at joints

Stepped Footing

From the Department of Housing and Urban Development's 1982 Minimum Property Standards:

"The horizontal distance between steps shall not be less than 2 feet.

"Stepped footings shall be poured monolithically with the vertical surface the same width as the footing and a minimum of 6 inches thick."

If a masonry wall is to be placed on a stepped footing, the footing should fit with masonry courses.

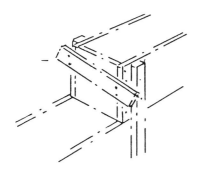

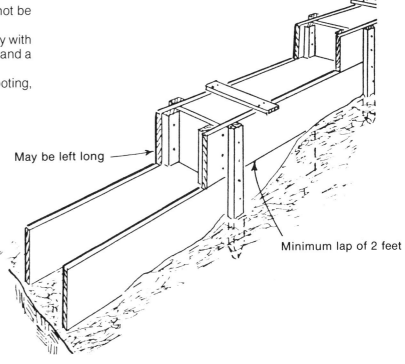

May be left long

Minimum lap of 2 feet

Corner Fastening

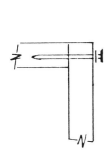

Poor, nail may withdraw.

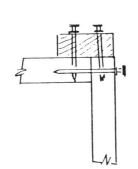

Better, gives lateral resistance in both directions.

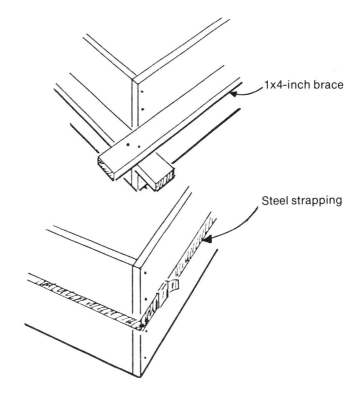

1x4-inch brace

Steel strapping

Forming Curbs and Gutters

Curbs can be finish-shaped with a darby or hand float. Driveway entrance curbs may not require a templet. Sometimes entrance curbs can be shaped entirely with a brickmason's trowel if the concrete has low slump.

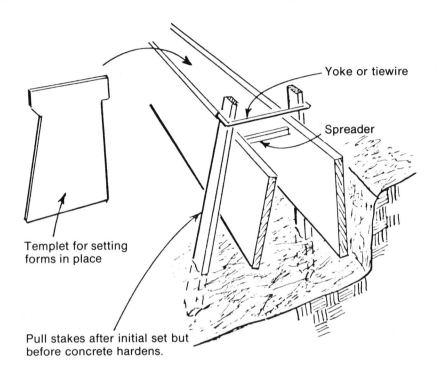

Yoke or tiewire

Spreader

Templet for setting forms in place

Pull stakes after initial set but before concrete hardens.

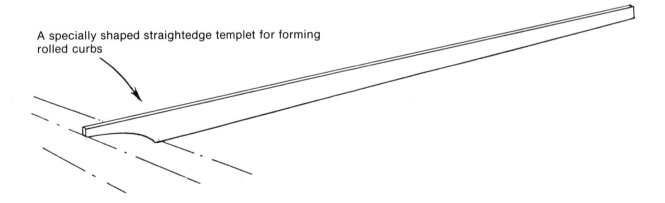

A specially shaped straightedge templet for forming rolled curbs

Forming a Slab on Grade

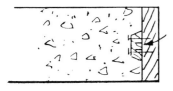

After the grade is marked on the end stakes, stretch a line for setting the form.

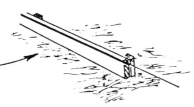

Put stake at all butt joints.

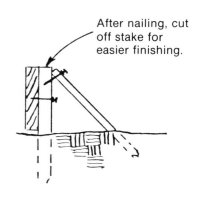

After nailing, cut off stake for easier finishing.

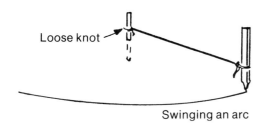

When forming a concrete construction joint, saw cuts here will make stripping easier. Metal keys and premolded keys (left in slab permanently) are also available.

Wood divider can be used for a control joint.

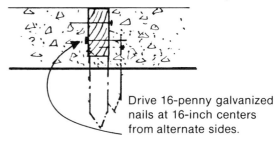

Drive 16-penny galvanized nails at 16-inch centers from alternate sides.

Forming a Curved Slab or Curb

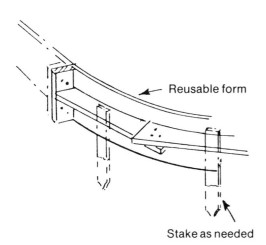

Loose knot

Swinging an arc

Reusable form

Stake as needed

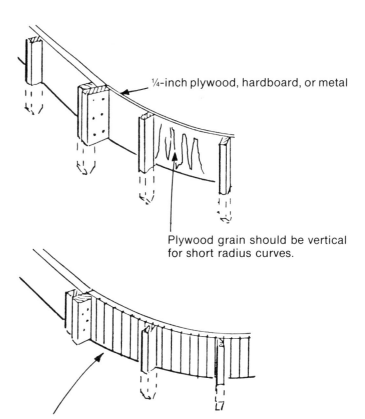

¼-inch plywood, hardboard, or metal

Plywood grain should be vertical for short radius curves.

For easy bending, ¾-inch material can be kerfed. Sometimes the bottom is kerfed on uneven ground. Soaking the wood overnight makes bending easier.

15

Forming Walls

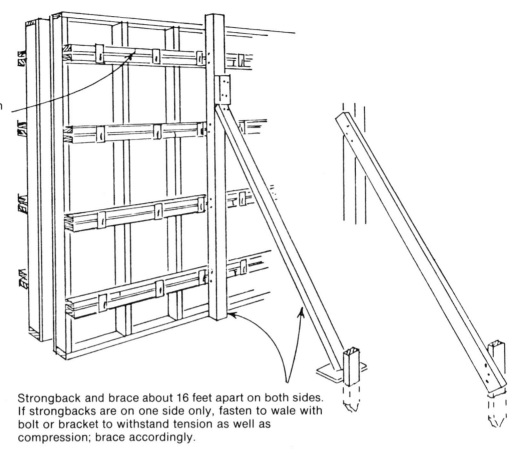

Stagger wale joints with minimum of two ties between joints.

Strongback and brace about 16 feet apart on both sides. If strongbacks are on one side only, fasten to wale with bolt or bracket to withstand tension as well as compression; brace accordingly.

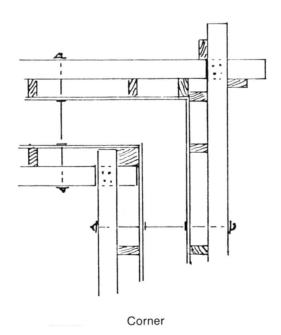

Corner

Reusable Job-Built Plywood Form Panels

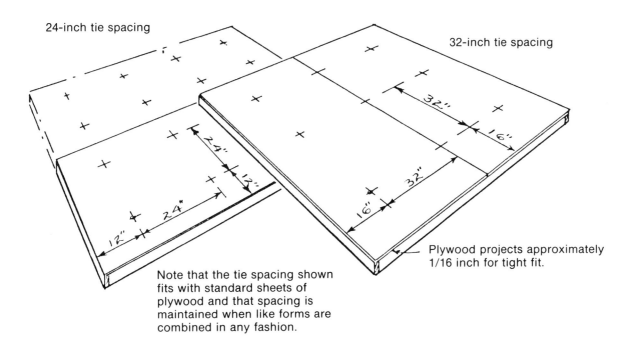

24-inch tie spacing

32-inch tie spacing

24"

12"

24"

12"

32"

16"

32"

16"

Plywood projects approximately 1/16 inch for tight fit.

Note that the tie spacing shown fits with standard sheets of plywood and that spacing is maintained when like forms are combined in any fashion.

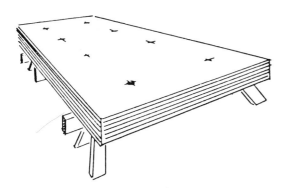

Drill holes in many sheets at the same time.

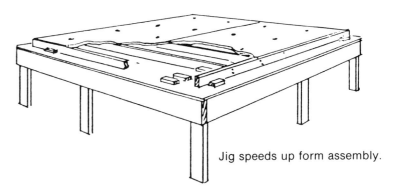

Jig speeds up form assembly.

Forming Door and Window Openings

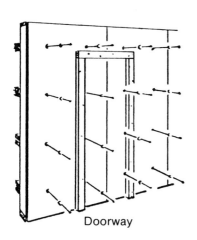

Doorway

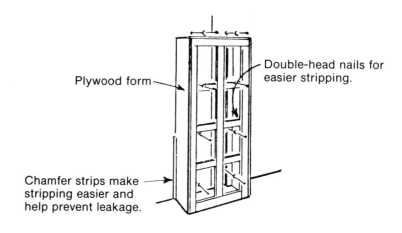

Plywood form

Double-head nails for easier stripping.

Chamfer strips make stripping easier and help prevent leakage.

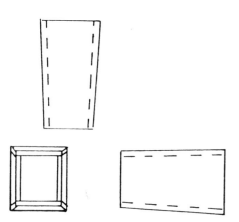

Form for small openings tapered for easy removal.

Window opening

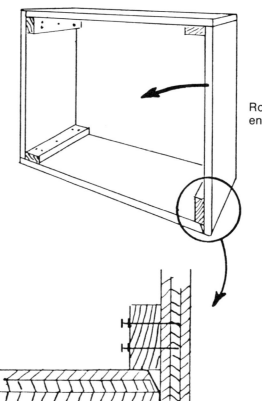

Rotate around beveled end to strip easily.

Single-Wall Forming

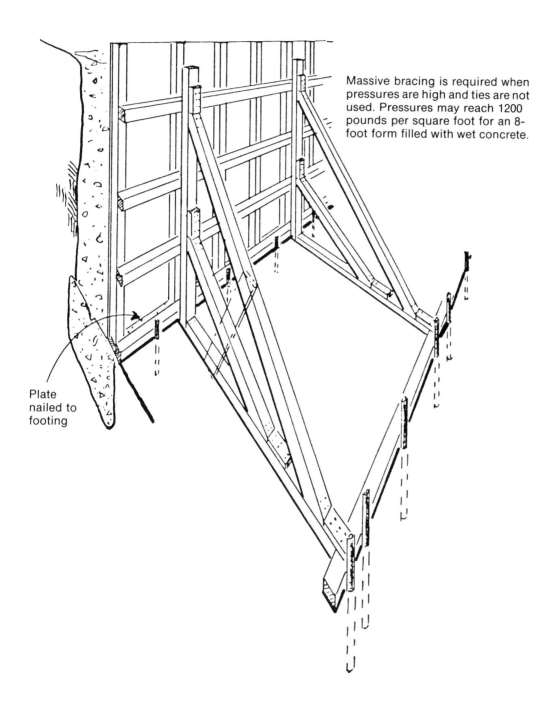

Massive bracing is required when pressures are high and ties are not used. Pressures may reach 1200 pounds per square foot for an 8-foot form filled with wet concrete.

Plate nailed to footing

Forming Stairs

Typical Low Exterior Stairs

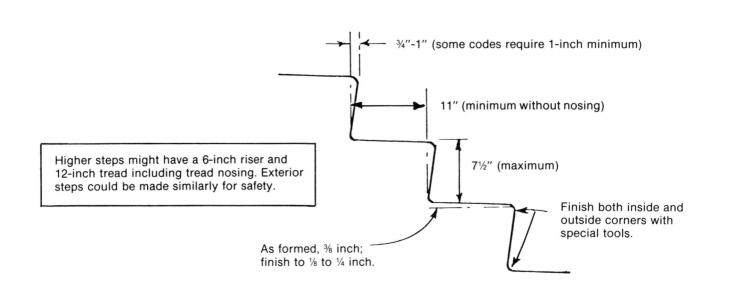

Fill with rubble such as stones or broken concrete but keep to a minimum of 6 inches from forms.

Space studs about 2 feet on center with ⅝-inch plywood.

Plywood for skirt boards is ½ to ¾ inch.

About ⅜-inch slope; finish to ⅛-inch slope.

¾″-1″

Two-inch material is actually 1½ inches thick. Reinforce it if it is longer than 4 feet.

Double-headed nails hold riser form.

Bevel for easier finishing.

¾″-1″ (some codes require 1-inch minimum)

11″ (minimum without nosing)

7½″ (maximum)

Higher steps might have a 6-inch riser and 12-inch tread including tread nosing. Exterior steps could be made similarly for safety.

As formed, ⅜ inch; finish to ⅛ to ¼ inch.

Finish both inside and outside corners with special tools.

Riser Bracing for Wide Stairs

Bracing should be used with riser forms when—
1. Riser form material is less than 1 inch thick for stairs that are 3 feet wide.
2. Riser form material is 2 inches thick (1½ inches actually) and spans more than 4 feet.

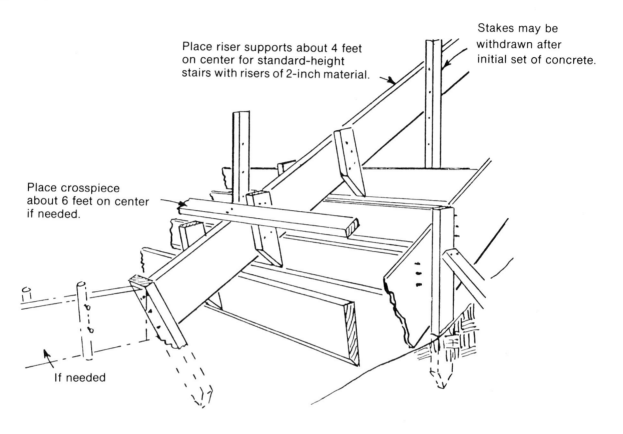

Place riser supports about 4 feet on center for standard-height stairs with risers of 2-inch material.

Stakes may be withdrawn after initial set of concrete.

Place crosspiece about 6 feet on center if needed.

If needed

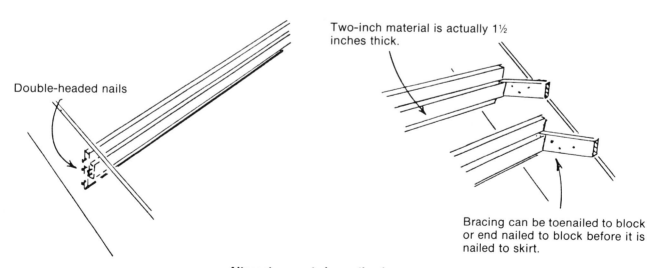

Double-headed nails

Two-inch material is actually 1½ inches thick.

Bracing can be toenailed to block or end nailed to block before it is nailed to skirt.

Alternate ways to brace the riser

Fastening Riser Form to Concrete or Masonry Wall

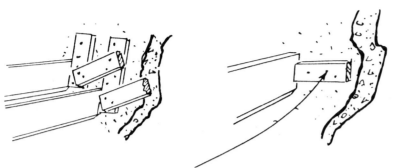

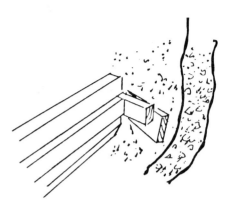

Use hardened nails such as concrete or case-hardened cut nails to fasten blocks to concrete.

Alternate: Wedge the block in place.

Stair Support

Stairs for both new and old construction should rest on firm supports—undisturbed soil or compacted fill at least 6 inches below the frostline to prevent settling, cracking, and pulling away from the building.

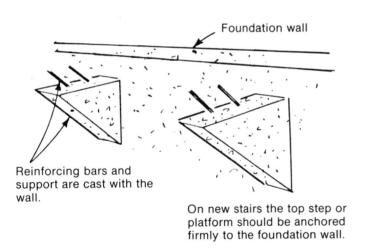

Foundation wall

Reinforcing bars and support are cast with the wall.

On new stairs the top step or platform should be anchored firmly to the foundation wall.

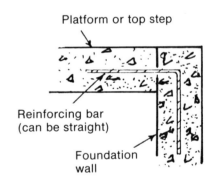

Platform or top step

Reinforcing bar (can be straight)

Foundation wall

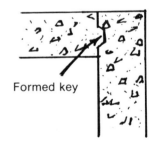

Formed key

Alternate ways to fasten to new construction

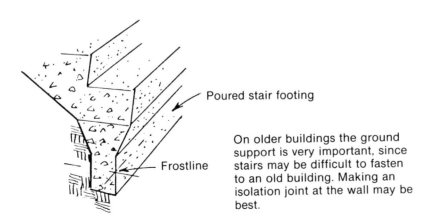

Poured stair footing

Frostline

On older buildings the ground support is very important, since stairs may be difficult to fasten to an old building. Making an isolation joint at the wall may be best.

Open Stairs*

Stairs supported at the top and bottom must be designed structurally according to span and load.

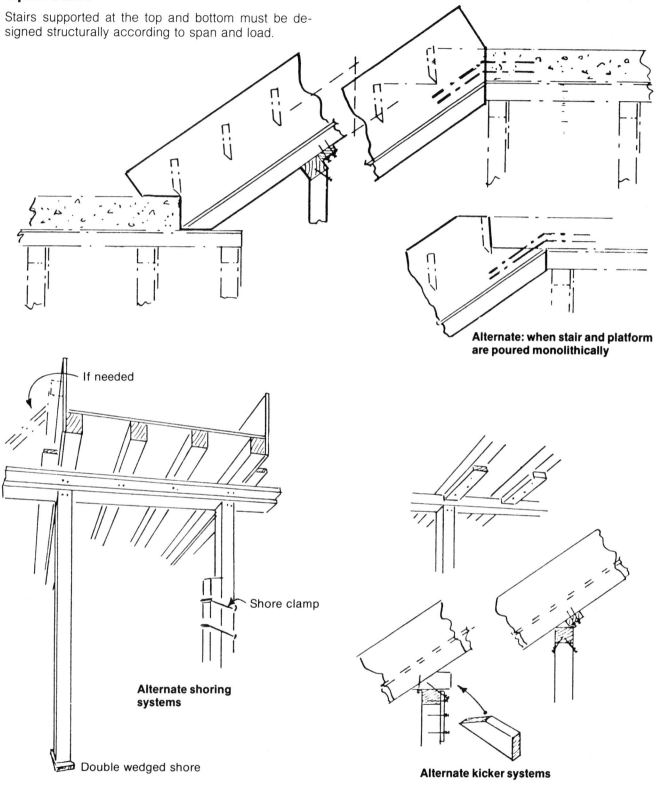

Alternate: when stair and platform are poured monolithically

If needed

Shore clamp

Alternate shoring systems

Double wedged shore

Alternate kicker systems

*For other form sketches—including columns, beams, structural slabs, special stairs, curved walls, and precast walls—and for information on how to design and size forms, see *Form Builders Manual,* National Association of Home Builders, Washington, D. C., 1979, 140 pages.

Jointing

The three basic joints and their functions:

Control Joints determine where cracks form.

Isolation Joints allow relative movement of sections of concrete without causing cracks.

Construction Joints connect hardened concrete from one pour to a later pour.

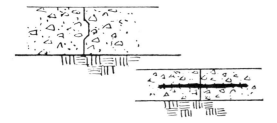

Control Joints

The control joint needs to be made deep enough—one-quarter the slab depth—so that the cracks do not go elsewhere. If the control joint is too deep, the concrete sections may not remain at the same level.

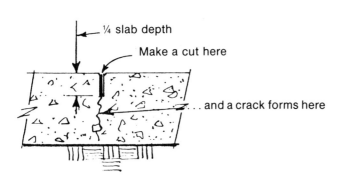

¼ slab depth

Make a cut here

...and a crack forms here

Locating Control Joints

Control joints are placed where stresses accumulate because highly stressed spots are likely to crack.

Typically, control joints should be spaced 10 to 20 feet apart, making concrete sections as nearly square as possible.

If the sections cannot be square, longer sides should never be more than 1½ times the length of the shorter sides.

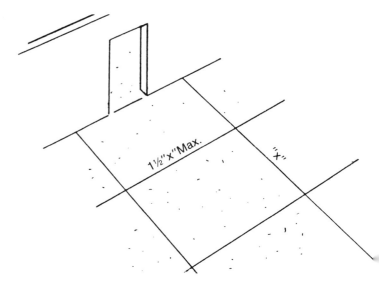

1½"X"Max.

"X"

The actual joint spacing can be influenced by many things, including—

- Proportion of water in the mix. More water may mean more cracks, thus the need for more control joints.
- Weather conditions. High temperature and low humidity may mean more cracks and the need for more control joints.
- Aggregate. The type and size of aggregate may influence cracking and thus control joint spacing (see Table 2).

Table 2.

Type of coarse aggregate	Joint spacing* (feet)
Crushed granite (1½" min.)	25
Crushed limestone	20
Crushed flinty limestone	20
Calcareous gravel	20
Siliceous gravel	15
Gravel (less than ¾")	15
Slag	15

*Joint spacing can be increased by using wire mesh in the slab. Sever the mesh completely within several inches of each side of the joint. A 35-foot interval requires 6x6—W2.0xW2.0 mesh while 45-foot spacing requires 6x6—W2.9xW2.9 mesh.

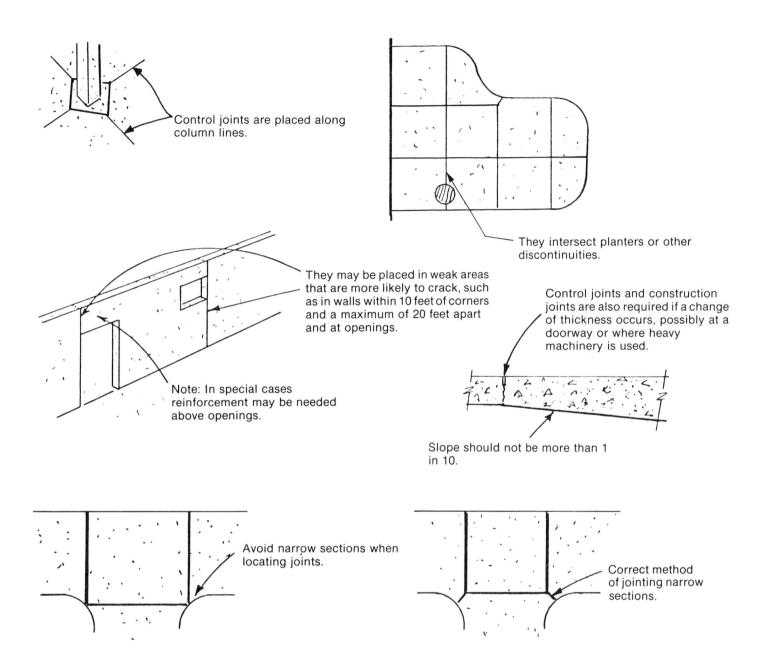

Control joints are placed along column lines.

They intersect planters or other discontinuities.

They may be placed in weak areas that are more likely to crack, such as in walls within 10 feet of corners and a maximum of 20 feet apart and at openings.

Note: In special cases reinforcement may be needed above openings.

Control joints and construction joints are also required if a change of thickness occurs, possibly at a doorway or where heavy machinery is used.

Slope should not be more than 1 in 10.

Avoid narrow sections when locating joints.

Correct method of jointing narrow sections.

Control Joints for Topping Slabs

A bonded topping joint should be at least as wide as the base slab joint, be directly over the base joint, and extend through the topping.

An unbonded topping should be free to move independently of the base; therefore, the joints need not line up. The topping joint should be at least half the thickness of the topping.

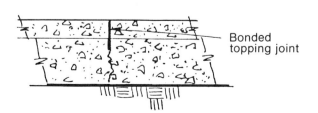

Bonded topping joint

Control Joints for Curbs

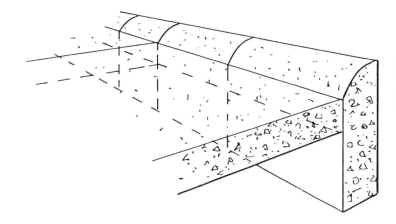

Continue the street control joints through the curb, even though the curb may have additional joints.

Cutting Control Joints

First dislodge the aggregate, and

Then use a special joint tool

Divider strips of decay-resistant wood such as heart cedar, heart redwood, or treated wood may be used for control joints.

For detailed guidelines on cutting control joints, including sawing joints, see "Finishing the Concrete," starting on page 39.

Sealing Control Joints

Seal control joints if they are apt to spall because of dirt, debris, or ice. Spalling may occur in driveways exposed to freeze and thaw and to heavy weights.

Many sealant materials are available, including polymers combined with coal tar, urethane, rubberized materials, asphalt combined with elastomeric polymers, wood, and plastics. The architect or owner may specify the sealant. If it is not specified, builders should consult local suppliers about the appropriate sealant to use.

Notes on sealing joints:

- Seal the joint flush with or slightly below the surface.
- Delay sealing as long as possible to allow the concrete to gain strength and the joint to open up as much as possible—usually a wait of 6 months.
- Do not use liquid curing compounds or other materials unless they work well with the joint sealant.
- Blow clean or vacuum clean the joint before sealing.

Structural Slabs and Control Joints

Structural slabs contain reinforcing steel and are typically unsupported underneath. These slabs must be continuous between supports and should not have control joints. They may develop fine cracks but the steel should keep large cracks from forming.

Occasionally, a structural slab is built on grade, perhaps in a flood-prone area or on unstable soil. An engineer may or may not specify joints in such a situation, depending on the design.

Wire mesh in the usual amounts does not create a structural slab, and control joints are needed. The mesh should not lap at joints.

Basement Slabs and Control Joints

Control joints are often omitted in basement slabs except when required by code. The basement area is usually small and at a relatively uniform temperature and major cracking is less likely. Still, cracks do occur, especially if the slabs are irregularly shaped and control joints will make the cracks less noticeable. If the slab is to be covered, say with tile or carpet, control joints are not needed.

Isolation Joints

Use isolation joints between concrete sections that need to move relative to each other.

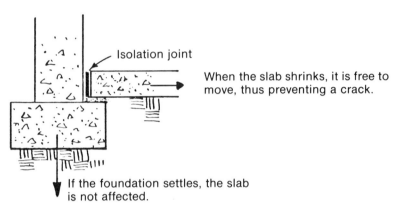

Isolation joint

When the slab shrinks, it is free to move, thus preventing a crack.

If the foundation settles, the slab is not affected.

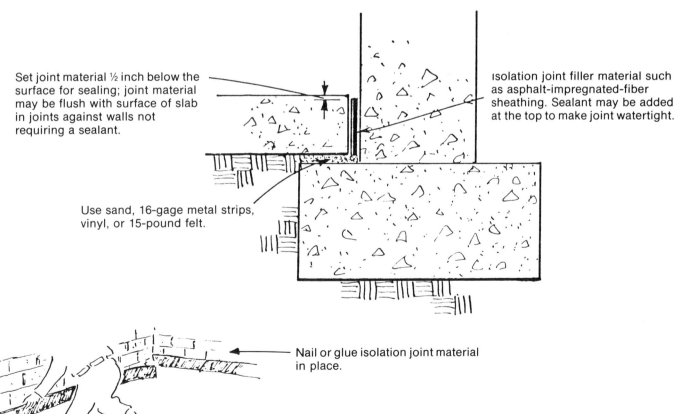

Set joint material ½ inch below the surface for sealing; joint material may be flush with surface of slab in joints against walls not requiring a sealant.

Isolation joint filler material such as asphalt-impregnated-fiber sheathing. Sealant may be added at the top to make joint watertight.

Use sand, 16-gage metal strips, vinyl, or 15-pound felt.

Nail or glue isolation joint material in place.

An Alternate Way to Form Isolation Joints

Wedge during construction. . .

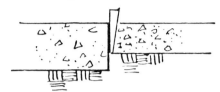

. . .add joint sealer afterward.

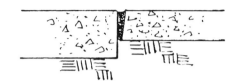

Other Examples of Isolation Joint Locations

If a walk abuts a doorway, use an isolation joint. Keep the walk a bit lower, so that if it heaves because of frost, it will not block the door.

walk

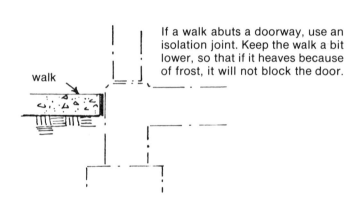

walk

drive

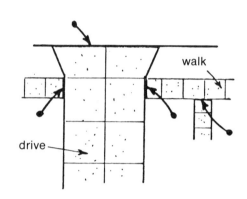

Arrows indicate isolation joints.

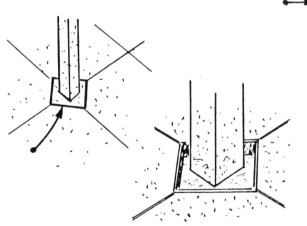

Isolation joint at column

patio

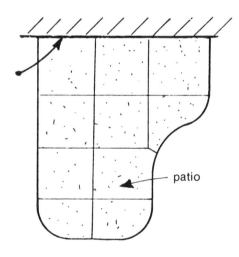

Isolation joints are also needed around rigid objects such as pipe columns, drains, fireplugs, manholes, and utility poles.

No box-out is needed if floor is to be covered with tile or carpet.

Construction Joints

Sometimes concreting must be interrupted—say at the end of the day—and a joint is required to tie the slab to the next day's pour. This is a construction joint.

Though a true construction joint is bonded so that it does not move at all, bonding usually is not necessary. Instead, the construction joint is made to work as a control joint, allowing horizontal but not vertical movement. A bondbreaker must be used at the joint to be sure it can move. An unbonded construction joint should be placed at a control joint location.

To make a true, rigid construction joint that does not move in any direction, steel reinforcing bars—called tie-bars—may be used.

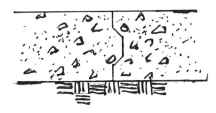

A typical construction joint is keyed so that neither side rises up past the other, and yet each side is free to move horizontally.

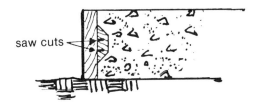

saw cuts

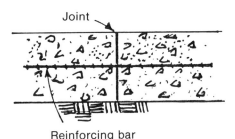

Joint

Reinforcing bar

Making Concrete Watertight

Generally, the same things that make concrete strong and crack resistant make it watertight, including—

- Low water-cement ratio: 0.50 by weight
- Good cement proportions: 6 bags per cubic yard of concrete for 1-inch-maximum aggregate
- Entrained air: 6 ± 1 percent for 1-inch aggregate
- Nonporous aggregate
- Handling concrete in a way that avoids segregation
- Good curing: 7 to 14 days

Watertightness should not be confused with the passage of water vapor. Even very good concrete will allow the passage of some water vapor.

Certain admixtures called dampproofing or permeability-reducing agents may reduce water passage in poorly made concretes such as those with a high water-cement ratio, low cement content, or excessive fines. However, the Portland Cement Association maintains that some of these agents may actually increase water transmission in well-proportioned mixes, since more mixing water may be needed.*

Good site drainage is very important in the overall waterproofing measures. The site should slope at least ⅝ inch per foot away from the house.

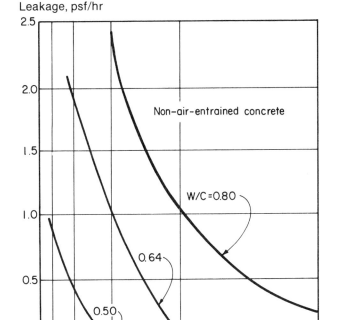

Leakage, psf/hr

Days of moist curing

How water-cement ratio (w/c) and curing affect watertightness.

*See *Design and Control of Concrete Mixtures*, 12th edition, Portland Cement Association, Skokie, Illinois, 1979, page 54.

Special Waterproofing Measures

Even if the basic concrete is sound, special waterproofing measures may be needed—especially if the site is unusually wet—since the best concrete can develop some cracks. The following measures help control moisture in special cases.

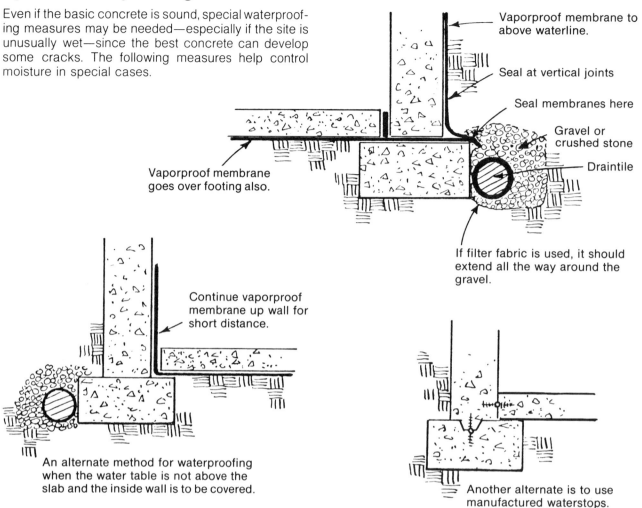

Vaporproof membrane to above waterline.

Seal at vertical joints

Seal membranes here

Gravel or crushed stone

Draintile

Vaporproof membrane goes over footing also.

If filter fabric is used, it should extend all the way around the gravel.

Continue vaporproof membrane up wall for short distance.

An alternate method for waterproofing when the water table is not above the slab and the inside wall is to be covered.

Another alternate is to use manufactured waterstops.

Waterproofing a Slab*

A vapor barrier to waterproof a concrete slab can be an asphaltic curing compound or a sheet material such as polyethylene film, rubber, or asphalt. The base slab usually cures well because of the barrier, thereby gaining strength and watertightness. This system, however, is labor costly because two slabs must be placed rather than one.

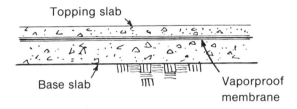

Topping slab

Base slab

Vaporproof membrane

VAPOR BARRIER RATINGS

Material	Perm rating
15-pound roofing felt	0.6 to 2.0
6-mil polyethylene film	0.06
55-pound roofing felt	0.03 to 0.08
Butyl rubber sheeting	0.002
⅛-inch asphalt panels	0

NOTE: *Perm* refers to vapor transmission. The lower the perm rating, the better the barrier.

15-pound roofing felt. This roofing felt is a relatively inexpensive barrier, but it is not very effective and does not last long. Sections should be lapped 4 to 6 inches and sealed with hot asphalt.

55-pound roofing felt. A 55-pound felt is much more effective than 15-pound felt, but it does not last long either.

Polyethylene film. Polyethylene film is very low in cost but is easily punctured during installation. Wide sheets should be used and lap joints avoided. If lap joints must be used, they should be at least 6 inches wide. Sometimes builders spread sand over the gravel or crushed-stone fill to avoid puncturing the film. Polyethylene-coated kraft paper is more durable and has a comparable perm rating.

Butyl rubber sheeting. Butyl sheeting is a good rugged, long lasting barrier. It is expensive, however, and may need to be prefabricated for the job. Splices are sealed with an adhesive.

⅛-inch asphalt paneling. Asphalt paneling is very effective, rugged, and less likely to be damaged by construction work. The panels are 4x8-foot sheets that are installed either by lapping or butt-jointing with 8-inch-wide strips overlaying the joints. The joints or strips are sealed with hot asphalt or asphalt mastic.

---

*Section R-603.2 of the One-and Two-Family Dwelling Code, developed by the Council of American Building Officials (CABO), requires that a vapor barrier be placed between a 4-inch-granular base course and the concrete floor slab.

Waterproofing Wall Joints

Control joints in concrete walls may be at openings, within 10 feet of corners, and a maximum of 20 feet apart otherwise.

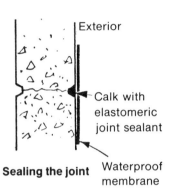

A ¾-inch wood strip beveled for easy removal is fine for 6-inch-thick walls, but total reduction of wall section must equal ¼ the wall thickness to make the control joint work.

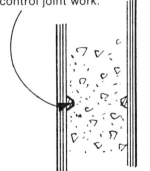

Exterior

Calk with elastomeric joint sealant

Sealing the joint   Waterproof membrane

Forming the joint

Making basements watertight requires special attention to details. *Basement Water Leakage: Causes, Prevention, and Correction** includes design information for drainage by sump or sump pump, but it does not discuss concrete technology. For further information on making basements watertight, see *Concrete Basements for Residential and Light Building Construction*** and *Joints in Walls Below Ground*.†

For flood-prone areas refer to *Manual for the Construction of Residential Basements in Non-Coastal Flood Environs*, developed by the NAHB Research Foundation, Inc., for the Department of Housing and Urban Development.††

---

*National Association of Home Builders, Washington, D.C.
**Portland Cement Association, IS208B, Skokie, Illinois, 1980, 8 pages.
†Portland Cement Association, CR059T, Skokie, Illinois, 1982, 14 pages.
††To obtain copies write to: Department of Housing and Urban Development, Federal Insurance Administration, 451 7th Street, S.W., Washington, D.C. 20410.

Layout Guidelines for Concrete Slabs

Recommended Slopes

Driveways, Patios, Sidewalks

Always slope a driveway so that water runs away from the house. A slope may need to be increased to around ⅝ inch per foot so that it is compatible with the earth slope. The minimum slope recommended by the Portland Cement Association is ¼ inch per foot. Slopes are exaggerated in the sketches.

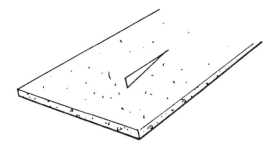

The slope may be toward the street

from one side to the other   to both sides from the middle   to the middle from both sides

Basement Slab

Basement slabs should slope at least ⅛ inch per foot toward basement doors, sumps, or drains.

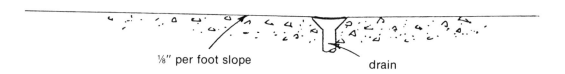

⅛" per foot slope   drain

If the slab is to be thicker in some places, say at a doorway that will carry heavy traffic, the slope should be gradual and have a joint at the transition to reduce the likelihood of cracking.

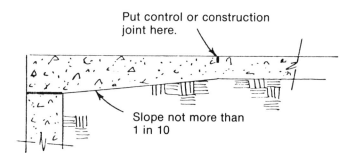

Put control or construction joint here.

Slope not more than 1 in 10

Recommended Thicknesses

Driveways: To be used by cars only, 4 inches; cars and trucks, 5 inches. Patios, floor slabs (including garage and basement), and sidewalks: 4 inches.

A lesser thickness of about 3 inches may be satisfactory if (1) the subgrade is firm and uniform, (2) the concrete has a low water-cement ratio and is well cured, and (3) it is not to receive heavy loads. Always check code requirements.

Setting the Grade

Using Transit or Builder's Level

Set the end stakes with a transit or builder's level, allowing for slope; then stretch a string for intermediate stakes.

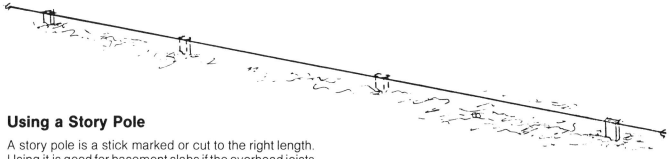

Using a Story Pole

A story pole is a stick marked or cut to the right length. Using it is good for basement slabs if the overhead joists are in place. Measure down from these joists with the story pole and set stakes around the entire slab area. Be sure to allow slope for drainage.

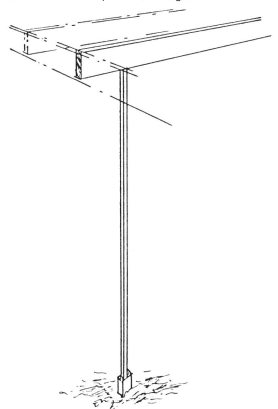

Dots and Wet Screeds

Setting the dot is one of the most efficient methods for setting the grade for flatwork. It is similar to the method plasterers use to set a thickness. Stakes are not needed.

Using dots instead of grade stakes is fast and cost-effective. The technique is particularly good to avoid puncturing polyethylene film.

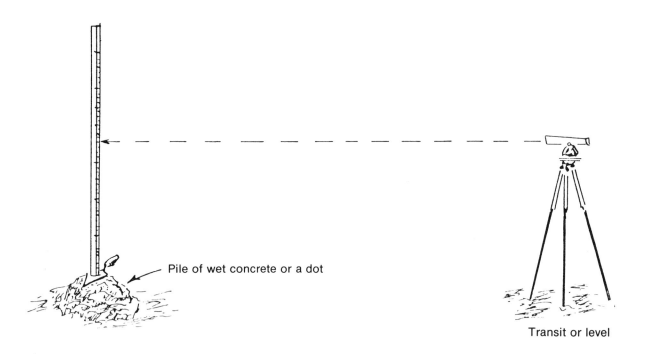

Pile of wet concrete or a dot

Transit or level

If side forms are in place, set the dot with a string.

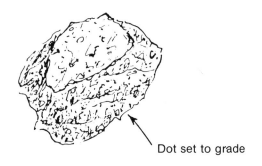

Dot set to grade

A wet screed is a row of wet concrete bridging between the concrete dots. Stakes can be used instead of dots.

After the wet screed is struck off to grade, concrete is placed between the screeds to fill the bay.

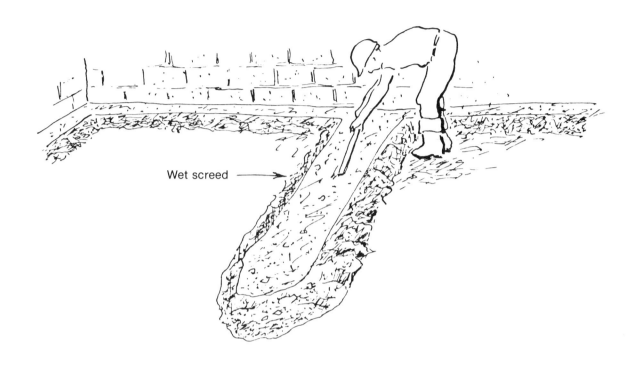

Wet screed ——→

Preparing the Subgrade

The basic rule for preparing a subgrade is to keep it uniform in—

- Firmness
- Grade
- Dampness

If the subgrade is not uniform, the concrete will be under more stress and may develop cracks.

Fill

Sometimes granular fill is used as a subbase or to fill low spots. Use sand, crushed stone, gravel, or slag. Do not use cinders, clay, or vegetation such as leaves, because they will not give firm and uniform support. The fill should be a 4- to 6-inch layer on the same slope as the finished concrete. Earthfill that is used for low spots should be the same type with the same moisture content as the surrounding soil. All fills should be well tamped. Hand tampers are inexpensive and are available from tool companies.

Dampening

Dampen the subgrade before placing concrete. Dampening keeps moisture from being drawn too rapidly from the concrete and helps avoid cracks and discoloration.

If possible, dampen the subgrade the night before or at least long enough before so that it is uniformly damp with no standing water when the concrete is poured.

The Subgrade in Hot Weather

In hot weather, dampen the subgrade well in advance of concrete placement. In some hot and arid parts of the country, workers dampen the subgrade for 24 hours before a pour. More typically, the dampening might be done the night before. The water should be well absorbed into the earth, with no standing water remaining at the time of concrete placement. The forms may need wetting too, especially if they are not treated with a release agent.

The Subgrade in Cold Weather

Do not place concrete on a frozen subgrade. A frozen subgrade is unstable and may either heave or settle unevenly, and the concrete will crack. Some builders avoid frozen subgrades by excavating the last foot or so the night before placing. Others may place straw or insulating blankets over the subgrade to prevent freezing. Still others may close in a basement, possibly even heating it, before pouring concrete.*

Earth Collapse

Sandy earth. Sandy earth is always dangerous. Even if it stands for some time after a vertical cut is made, sandy soil may fall at any time without warning. Sandy soil is in more danger of a fall from (a) moisture change such as a change in humidity or the water table (the level of free water in the ground); (b) vibration from blasting, traffic, or equipment; and (c) overloads of materials, equipment, or workers standing near the cut.

Clay soil. Clay soil is generally not as dangerous as sandy soil. Clay can usually stand a vertical cut. However, clay can be dangerous if the cut is over 8 feet deep or if it is soft, regardless of the amount of moisture present. If a 2x4 can be pushed into the clay, beware of a collapse. Added moisture may increase the danger.

Silty soil. Silt is a combination of sand and clay. Its resistance to collapse is uncertain, so treat it like sandy earth.

Loose fill of sandy earth or clay or silty soil behaves like sand and is dangerous.

Installing Reinforcement

Wire Mesh**

By far the worst—and probably the most typical and quickest—way to install wire mesh is to hook it while it is on the ground and pull it up to about 2 inches from the surface as the concrete is placed.

One disadvantage with this method is that the mesh can bring earth up into the concrete as it is pulled into place. Another disadvantage is that the mesh is seldom pulled to the correct height.

A good mesh-placing method is to place about half the concrete slab thickness, strike it off, place the mesh, and then place the remaining concrete and strike it off. This method gives good placement and keeps the mesh clean, but it is more costly.

An equally good method is to use concrete, steel, or plastic supports to chair up the mesh at the correct height. Do not use broken brick; it causes cracks because of its high water absorption.

Where to Place Mesh

According to the Wire Reinforcement Institute (WRI), the mesh should be placed 2 inches down from the surface to exert good control over cracking. It is placed at the middle of a 4-inch slab.

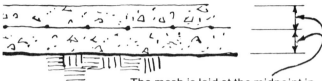

The mesh is laid at the midpoint in a 4-inch slab and 2 inches from the top in 5- and 6-inch slabs.

Control Joints and Mesh

Slabs with wire mesh require control joints, but the joints should not coincide with the lap of the mesh. If typical 6x6—W1.4xW1.4 mesh is used, stop the mesh several inches from each side of joints that are not more than 25 feet apart. (See "Locating Control Joints.")

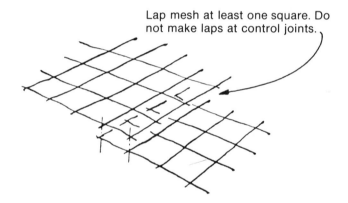

Lap mesh at least one square. Do not make laps at control joints.

Ductwork and Mesh

If a floor does not contain wire mesh elsewhere, the area over ducts should be reinforced. A 6x6—W1.4xW1.4 fabric may be used and should be extended 18 inches past the point where slab thickness returns to normal.

Size of Mesh

WRI recommends 6x6—W1.4xW1.4 mesh for sidewalks and patios and that wire spacing not exceed 6 inches in slabs less than 6 inches thick.

---

*See Department of Housing and Urban Development *All-Weather Homebuilding Manual.*

**The need for mesh in slabs on grade is often questioned, although it may have value if sized and placed properly. Mesh prevents cracks from spreading wider and keeps the aggregate interlocked at cracks and thus helps prevent displacement—important in meeting NAHB's Home Owners Warranty (HOW) program criteria. Fewer control joints are needed when mesh is used. (See "Wire Mesh," page 9, and "Locating Control Joints," page 24.) Some codes require the use of mesh.

Reinforcing Steel

Cover for Reinforcing Steel

When reinforcing steel is used in concrete placed directly on earth or fill; for example, footings or a slab poured on earth, the minimum cover should be 3 inches as shown in the sketch.

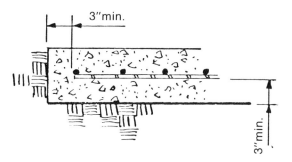

For concrete that is to be exposed to earth or weather, but not poured directly on earth, use 1½ or 2 inches of cover depending upon bar sizes as follows:

Reinforcing steel	Cover
#6 through #18 bars	2 inches
#5 bars, ⅝-inch wire and smaller	1½ inches

For concrete that is not to be exposed to weather and not to be in contact with the ground, such as slabs, walls, and joists, use:

Reinforcing steel	Cover
#14 and #18 bars	1½ inches
#11 and smaller	¾ inches

Lapping Reinforcing Steel

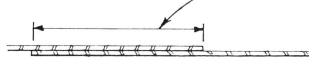

Lap at least 24 bar diameters, never less than 12 inches. Smooth bars are lapped even more.

The Concrete

The most convenient way to obtain concrete is to order it from a local ready mixed concrete supplier. The ingredients for ready mixed concrete are accurately measured, often in automated plants with computer equipment, and then mixed either at the plant or in a truck mixer, and delivered to the jobsite.

Ready mixed concrete producers will generally assist in the selection of appropriate mixes or in developing mixes to fill a builder's specific needs. Mixes proportioned to provide the strength levels shown in Table 3 are considered adequate for the applications shown. Local practices in ordering ready mixed concrete vary from area to area, but usually ordering is either by *performance* or by *prescription*.

Table 3. Guidelines for Selecting Concrete Strength (Recommended by National Ready Mixed Concrete Association)

Specified Compressive Strength (f'_c) at 28 days, psi*

Type or location of concrete construction	Regional weathering areas**			Design slump, (in.)
	Negligible	Moderate (air)	Severe (air)	
Basement walls and foundations not exposed to weather	2000	2500	2500	6 ± 1
Basement slabs and interior slabs on grade	2500	2500	2500	5 ± 1
Basement walls, foundations, exterior walls, and other concrete work exposed to weather	2500	3000 (5%-7%)	3000 (5%-7%)	6 ± 1
Driveways, curbs, walks, patios, porches, and unheated garage floors exposed to weather	2500	3000 (5%-7%)	3500 (5%-7%)	5 ± 1

*Generally specifications such as ASTM C94 permit 10 percent of the strength tests to fall below f'_c, but no tests can be more than 500 psi below.
**See map on page 38.

When selecting the type of concrete, builders should consider the durability and finishability needed for the job conditions.

In either method of ordering, builders should advise ready mixed concrete producers of the intended use for the concrete (such as a footing, sidewalk, or basement slab), the slump level desired, the maximum size of coarse aggregate, and the air content for air-entrained concrete. Quite often suppliers have standard mixes for specific applications (such as a sidewalk mix, a footing mix, or a county curb and gutter mix). By specifying its intended use, builders can help to ensure that the proper concrete is delivered.

When concrete is ordered by performance, strength level desired is specified by the builder, and the ready mixed concrete producer is responsible for proportioning and delivering a mixture that will yield the desired strength in a substantial majority of tests. For strength specifications to be meaningful, properly conducted strength tests are required.

When concrete is ordered by prescription, builders specify the weight of portland cement per cubic yard, maximum amount of mixing water, admixtures required, and possibly their dosage rates. In essence, the builders are accepting responsibility for the level of quality and performance. The ready mixed suppliers are responsible for accurately batching and adequately mixing the ingredients specified in the prescriptions.

Builders must also specify where and when concrete is to be delivered and the amount required. An order should specify about 5 percent more concrete than the computed volume of the forms to allow for spillage, form movement, and consolidation.

Concrete is a perishable product. To do a good concrete job, builders and ready mixed concrete suppliers must work together to minimize delays. Before the concrete arrives, builders should check their formwork to ensure that it is accurately set and adequately built to withstand the pressure of fresh concrete. They should make sure that an experienced crew is properly equipped to handle, place, finish, and cure the concrete and that the ready mixed concrete trucks have easy access to locations of the pours.

When the concrete arrives at a job, the builder should be given a delivery ticket with the following information:

- Class or designation of concrete conforming to the job specification (example: 3000 psi or a 5½-bag mix)
- Amount of concrete in cubic yards
- Time of loading (generally ready mixed concrete should be discharged from the truck within 1½ hours of loading)
- Water added by the builder (many ready mixed concrete producers require builders to sign for water added at their jobsites)

Upon arrival at the jobsite, one addition of water is permitted to bring the load to the specified slump. The water should be thoroughly mixed into the load and the concrete discharged as quickly as possible. Additional water added as a load is discharged can reduce the quality of the concrete. *Under no circumstances* should additional water be added to concrete that is over 1½ hours old.

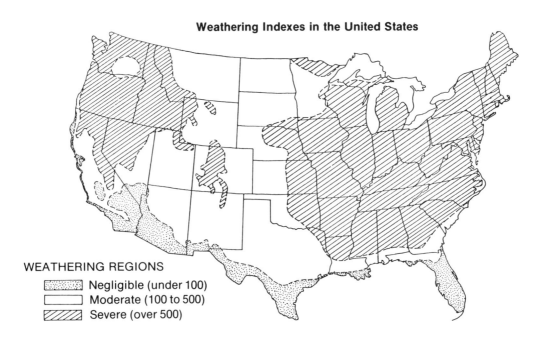

Weathering Indexes in the United States

WEATHERING REGIONS
- Negligible (under 100)
- Moderate (100 to 500)
- Severe (over 500)

The weathering index for any locality is the product of the average annual number of *freezing-cycle days* and the average annual *winter rainfall* in inches, defined as follows:*

A *freezing-cycle day* is any day during which the air temperature passes either above or below 32 F. The average number of freezing-cycle days in a year may be taken to equal the difference between the mean number of days during which the minimum temperature was 32 F or below and the mean number of days during which the maximum temperature was 32 F or below.

Winter rainfall is the sum, in inches, of the mean monthly corrected precipitation (rainfall) occurring during the period between and including the normal date of the first killing frost in the fall and the normal date of the last killing frost in the spring. The winter rainfall for any period is equal to the total precipitation less one tenth of the total fall of snow, sleet, and hail. Rainfall for a portion of a month is prorated.

The map indicates general areas of the United States in which concrete is subject to severe, moderate, and negligible weathering. The severe weathering region has a weathering index greater than 500. The moderate weathering region has a weathering index of 100 to 500. The negligible weathering region has a weathering index of less than 100.

---
*Data needed to determine the weathering index for any locality may be found or estimated from the tables of Local Climatological Data, published by the Weather Bureau, U.S. Department of Commerce.

Placing the Concrete

Place concrete as close as possible to its final position. Do not try to move it horizontally with a vibrator, jitterbug, rake, shovel, or anything else over long distances—especially if it is high slump. Working the concrete in this manner can result in segregation of the aggregate from the paste, or a thin watery paste may be worked to the surface that may later craze, dust, or scale.

Dump new concrete against the face of the previously placed concrete, rather than in separate piles. Separate piles can partially set up before they are joined to other concrete and may cause a poor bond, known as a cold joint.

Start placing concrete for walls at each end and work toward the middle; for slabs start placing at the edges and work toward the middle. Avoid collecting water at ends, in corners, and along form faces.

Use a baffle on slopes to avoid separation and accumulation of aggregate at the bottom of the slope. Place concrete on the lower part of the slope first and move upward.

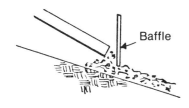

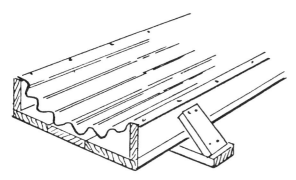

A piece of corrugated metal makes a good chute.

Remember to use only accepted concrete working tools such as short-handled square-end shovels or concrete rakes. Do not use yard rakes; they may increase segregation.

Strike off as the concrete is placed to avoid moving the concrete again later. Strike off a bit high to allow for later subsidence and avoid a dished surface near the edges.

Do not lay dots and wet screeds too far ahead of the placing operation. They may begin to set up and can create a cold joint.

Placing Concrete for Steps

Stair forms that are to be removed the same day may be wetted; those that are to stay in place several days should be coated with a form release agent.

To place the concrete, begin at the bottom step and work upward. Carefully spade or vibrate the mix, especially next to form faces. Each tread should be struck off level as it is filled. Forms should be tapped lightly to release air bubbles.

Cement Contact—Caution

Wet concrete can cause skin burns or dermatitis. Protect the skin with a long-sleeved shirt, boots, gloves, and kneepads.

Wash affected skin thoroughly with water and then apply vinegar. Lanolin or carbonated vaseline may help relieve irritation. Consult a physician if the condition persists.

If the eyes are affected, wash them with clean water. Do not use any other treatment without consulting a doctor. Do not rub the eyes.

Finishing the Concrete

The following comments are intended as a checklist for the supervisor to ensure good finishing techniques.*

The basic rule for good finishing: Do *nothing* to the concrete if bleed water is present.

Complete striking off and bullfloating before bleed water appears, and do not begin finish floating and troweling until after bleed water leaves.

If the concrete is worked with bleed water present, a water-rich mix that is sand heavy is created at the worst place—the surface. Dusting, scaling, and crazing are almost certain to result. For the same reason, do not add water to the surface for finishing ease.

Sometimes concrete begins to set up while bleed water is still present. In that case finishing must begin, and one of the following steps must be taken:

• Go out on the concrete on kneeboards and sweep off the water with a long trowel, darby, hairbroom, or squeegee.
• With one person at each end, drag the surface with a rubber hose.
• Lay damp burlap on the concrete and then spread cement on the burlap. Later, throw away the cement; the burlap can be washed and reused.

---

*For more details on cement masonry skills, see *Incentive Apprenticeship Training for Cement Masons*, National Association of Home Builders, Washington, D.C., 1979.

Do not add cement directly to the surface to take up the water; it will cause the surface to crack, craze, or dust after it dries. If air-entrained concrete is used with a low water-cement ratio, excess bleeding should be no problem.

Remember to avoid contact with wet concrete.

Striking Off and Bullfloating

Strikeoff should follow right after placing, and bullfloating right after strikeoff. Do not let any one finishing operation get too far ahead of the others. Complete bullfloating before bleed water appears.

To avoid segregation, do not jitterbug the plastic concrete to level it unless it is very low slump. If the finishers have trouble working the concrete into place, plasticizers and superplasticizers may help. (See page 6.)

Bullfloat perpendicular to the strikeoff direction. Bullfloat a second time perpendicular to the first bullfloating. These measures help to avoid dishing the surface. If dishing occurs anyway, the surface may need to be darbied.

A full strikeoff also will help avoid dishing near the edges. For more on dishing see "Edging" and "Making Control Joints," which follow.

Wood bullfloats tend to be better for opening up the concrete and letting bleed water out—for example, on concrete that is not air entrained and in cool or damp weather. Wood bullfloats are also better for sawing off and straightening the surface.

On the other hand, magnesium or aluminum bullfloats are easier to use on air-entrained concrete, and they help to avoid tearing the surface.

To save on labor and lessen segregation, do not work the concrete more than necessary.

Beware of the finisher's using a fresno for a bullfloat. The fresno is a long-handled trowel that tends to seal the surface and cause blisters if it is used as a bullfloat. Fresnos are used in place of bullfloats in special circumstances if the concrete surface needs to be sealed.

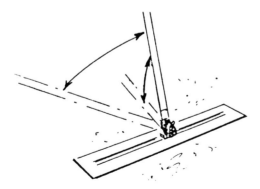

Fresno handles are often adjustable in two directions, and bullfloat handles usually are not.

Edging

Edging is easier if the aggregate is cut away from the form with a trowel beforehand. A good time to do this is right after bullfloating and before bleed water appears.

Wait until the concrete is ready for finishing before doing the edging. A good test for readiness is when the weight of a person standing on the concrete does not make footprints deeper than ¼ inch. Bleed water should be gone.

Use a wide-flanged edger for the first pass to prevent making a deep mark and to avoid sealing off the surface too much.

In very hot weather when the concrete is setting fast, the first pass with the edger can be run at the same time the aggregate is cut away with the trowel. This step should be taken soon after bullfloating.

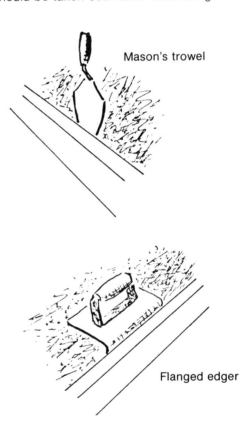

Mason's trowel

Flanged edger

Avoiding a High or Dished Edge

A concrete edge that slopes upward is called a dished edge. Ways to help prevent this condition include—

- After floating, use the back of the trowel to straighten the edge, and then finish the slab.
- Place a thin strip on the top of the form and remove it after the first floating-troweling. This leaves the concrete slightly high and lets the power float-trowel extend 4 to 6 inches past the edge.

Making Control Joints

For guidelines on laying out control joints, see the section "Jointing," page 24.

Control joints should be cut to one quarter of the slab depth. Finishers often do not go this deep since it requires more work. When they do not, the cracks go elsewhere. If the cut is too deep, aggregate interlock is lost and the concrete sections may then slip past each other vertically.

Remember that wire mesh should not be lapped at control joints.

The joints can be hand-tooled, sawed, or formed with lumber or prefinished strips that are left in place.

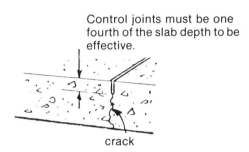

Control joints must be one fourth of the slab depth to be effective.

crack

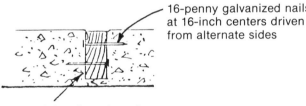

16-penny galvanized nails at 16-inch centers driven from alternate sides

Control joint of nondecaying 2x4 lumber

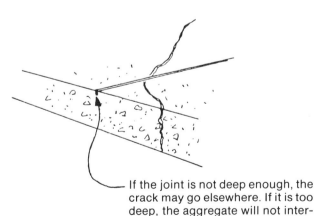

If the joint is not deep enough, the crack may go elsewhere. If it is too deep, the aggregate will not interlock and displacement can occur.

Hand-Tooling the Joint

Use the groover just before floating and troweling and again afterwards. Do not work on the concrete when bleed water is present.

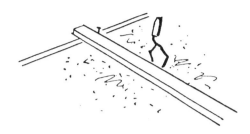

Using a trowel soon after bull-floating to dislodge aggregate makes using the groover much easier later.

Sawing the Joint

A sawed joint should be the same depth—one quarter the slab thickness—as a hand-tooled joint.

Saw the concrete as soon as it is firm enough to be sawed without dislodging any aggregate. Proper firmness occurs typically from 4 to 24 hours after the concrete is placed, but weather conditions may make the time longer or shorter. A slight raveling of the aggregate is all right and shows that the sawing is being done at about the right time.

Use an abrasive, nondiamond saw blade on green concrete that is set but not appreciably hardened. The loose particles in green concrete may tear the diamonds off a diamond blade.

Diamond blades are preferred for harder concrete and concrete with very hard aggregate. Use water for cooling when cutting with a diamond blade to avoid ruining the blade.

Sealing Control Joints

Remember to allow the joint time to widen from drying shrinkage of the concrete before sealing—about 6 months after curing. (See page 26 for guidelines.)

Floating and Troweling

Floating helps embed the aggregate; removes bumps, voids, and imperfections; and compacts the surface somewhat.

Troweling compacts, densifies, and hardens the surface, making it smoother and more wear resistant. On industrial floors with a lot of traffic, the slab might be troweled 5 to 10 times. For a typical residential floor slab, a floating and troweling followed by a second troweling may be enough.

Concrete is often troweled even if it is later broomed for slip resistance.

Sometimes the troweling may be omitted on areas such as driveways and sidewalks that do not need a dense surface. In that case a second floating may be necessary to get the desired texture.

When To Start

Wait to hand float and trowel until the concrete is firm enough so that a person's weight on it makes only a ¼-inch imprint. The concrete should be a bit firmer before power floating and troweling.

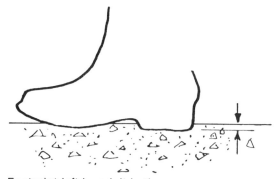

Footprint left by adult in the concrete should be no more than ¼ inch deep.

Bleed water should not be present on the surface. But lack of bleed water is not enough of a test for readiness, since air-entrained concrete and low-slump concrete may not bleed much.

In some cases the concrete starts to set up with bleed water present. In these instances the concrete can be finished but special measures are needed.

Spraying or sprinkling water on the surface to make finishing easier must never be done, since it may have the same effect as working the surface with bleed water

present: It can weaken the surface and cause dusting, scaling, or crazing.

Hand Floating and Troweling

Start with floating and then trowel flat. Use a smaller trowel for subsequent trowelings, and increase the angle slightly each time. Keep the angle small—never increase it more than ½ inch. If the angle is increased too much, a washboard or chatter effect leaves ripples that are very hard to remove; and even after the ripples are removed pinholes may remain.

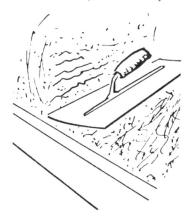

Too great a troweling angle leaves chatter marks that are hard to remove.

Use a magnesium float on air-entrained concrete. Wood may tear the surface too much.

Use a wood float on concrete that is not air-entrained or is high slump. Wood opens up the concrete, letting entrapped air escape, thereby helping prevent blisters. A wood float also makes a rough texture that allows better evaporation.

Do not overtrowel. Overtroweling can leave burn marks on the concrete, particularly if a steel trowel is used. Calcium chloride in the concrete may worsen this effect. Be particularly careful with white or colored concrete. Masons sometimes use plastic trowels or dampen the trowel to help avoid problems.

Power Floating and Troweling

Follow the same general blade-angle guidelines recommended for hand floating and troweling.

The concrete should be a bit harder before power floating than it is for hand floating. It is ready for power floating when an adult's weight makes about an ⅛-inch indentation.

Some experts recommend that the final troweling be done by hand, even if the slab is initially power troweled. Hand troweling provides a good final finish and may be less costly overall. Also, hand troweling finishes corners and other tight spots that a troweling machine cannot reach.

Finishing Stairs

Early Stripping Method

Strike off and darby the top-tread landing. Edge, then hand float and hand trowel when the concrete has set up enough to support an adult's weight and leave an impression no more than ¼ inch deep.

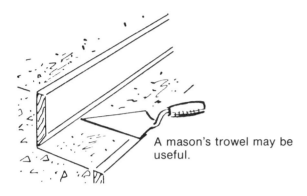

A mason's trowel may be useful.

Kneeboard

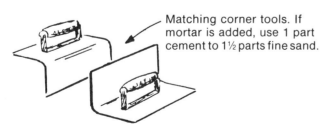

Matching corner tools. If mortar is added, use 1 part cement to 1½ parts fine sand.

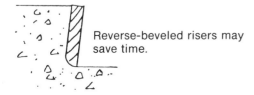

Reverse-beveled risers may save time.

Continue down the steps. Float each tread and edge with a ¼- to ½-inch-radius tool, then trowel.

Wait until the steps have set up enough so that they hold their shape when the riser boards are removed. The length of time varies depending on conditions. But do not wait too long.

When the steps have set up, remove the top riser form. Finish each step before going down to the next one.

After troweling, draw a damp brush across the riser and the tread to produce a uniform-looking nonskid surface. This procedure is similar to brooming a slab.

Move down, remove the next riser form, and finish that step. Work quickly so that the lower steps can be finished before the concrete sets too hard.

The sidewalls can also be finished the same day. First float and then plaster with a ⅛- to ¼-inch layer of mortar. The mortar should be spread with a trowel and then floated with a cork or sponge-rubber float. The surface may be troweled, brushed, or swirled. As an alternative, sidewall forms may be left in place several days for better curing. A grout cleandown may be needed to give the final finish. (See also "Grout Cleandown, Sacking, and Rubbing" following.)

Late Stripping Method

Leaving the forms on the stairs for a few days will provide added insulation in cold weather and thus speed up strength gain.

Float, edge, trowel, and brush while the forms, including risers, are still in place. Correctly finishing near the bottom of riser forms is very important to avoid later trouble.

After removing each form, chip or grind off with a handstone all small projections. Any honeycomb areas should be chipped out and patched with a stiff mortar to match the mortar used in the concrete. These operations will be minimized if care is taken in forming and placing the concrete. If risers and sidewalls are not uniform in color when the forms are stripped, a grout cleandown can be used.

Grout Cleandown, Sacking, and Rubbing

Concrete surfaces may have blotches, a slight film, mortar stains from leaks in the forms, or small pits. Grout cleandown, sacking, and rubbing help remedy these conditions.

After defects have been repaired, saturate the surface thoroughly with water. A grout of 1 part portland cement and 1½ to 2 parts of fine sand should be applied uniformly by brushing, spraying, or floating with a rubber float. The mixture should completely fill small voids in the surface. White portland cement is often used for about one quarter of the cement in the grout to give a lighter color. Float the surface vigorously with a rubber or wood float immediately after applying the grout. Then rub the surface with clean dry burlap. No visible film of grout should remain on the surface after the rubbing. Grout should not remain on the surface overnight as it will become too difficult to remove. This work should be done in the shade and preferably in cool, damp weather.

A similar procedure is to apply the grout by rubbing it on with burlap or a sponge-rubber float, completely filling all pits. When the grout dries sufficiently so that it does not smear, the excess is removed by rubbing with clean burlap. Curing should then be continued for 2 days.

With both methods, rewet and rerub the surface if necessary.

Placing and Finishing in Hot, Dry, or Windy Weather

Concrete sets up much faster in hot weather. Evaporation is also much faster in hot, dry, or windy weather. Water evaporates nine times faster in a 25-mph wind than it does with no wind. Losing control of concrete is easy under such conditions, and therefore special techniques are required, including changes in mix design and admixtures. The mix may need to be cooled, and special curing procedures used.

Placing and finishing procedures must also accommodate hot, dry, and windy weather. General guidelines include—

- Planning ahead. When the concrete arrives no time can be wasted; the forms and subgrade must be prepared, tools and workers standing by, curing materials at hand, and windbreaks and sunshades constructed if they are needed.
- Plan the best time of day to place the concrete. In hot weather this time may be very early in the morning or late in the evening.
- Dampen the subgrade well in advance of placing. In some hot and dry areas of the country, the subgrade is dampened for 2 or 3 days in advance of placing. More typically, dampening is done the night before. A damp subgrade keeps water from being drawn too rapidly from the underside of the concrete. Water should not be standing on the subgrade when the concrete mix is placed.
- Be sure the mix is modified appropriately and is not too hot.
- After placing and during finishing, evaporation must be controlled. Use windbreaks, sunshades, polyethylene sheets, wet burlap, or waterproof paper to cover the concrete during finishing. A fine water spray from a fog nozzle may be used but is not recommended, since water can build up and cause surface crazing, dusting, or scaling and good control and uniformity would be a problem.
- Begin curing immediately after finishing, using any required special techniques.

Plastic shrinkage cracks may form, particularly when evaporation is rapid. For controlling techniques, see "Plastic Shrinkage Cracks," page 54.

Placing and Finishing in Cold Weather

Just as heat speeds up hydration, cold weather slows it down. Concrete almost stops gaining strength when temperatures are near freezing. In cold weather, the concrete may freeze before it gains sufficient strength and watertightness. Good curing may help reclaim some strength, but special precautions should be taken when the air temperature is 40 degrees or less, especially if the temperature is falling.

Guidelines for placing and finishing in cold weather include—

- Preparing in advance. Have items such as insulating blankets, heated enclosures, and admixtures at hand for an emergency.
- Do not place concrete on a frozen subgrade, or on a subgrade that is likely to freeze. A frozen subgrade is unstable. It may either heave or settle unevenly and crack the concrete.
- Use the right concrete mixture. Use a low-slump mix with air entrainment if the concrete is to be exposed to freezing and thawing or deicers.

High-early-strength cement and admixtures such as calcium chloride accelerate strength gain to help prevent damage due to freezing.

- Use heated concrete. Heated concrete is available from many ready mix plants located in cold climates.
- Do not overtrowel concrete containing calcium chloride as this is likely to discolor the concrete.

Special curing measures such as insulation and extra heating are needed in cold weather, especially during the first days after pouring. Accelerators or high-early-strength cement can also be used.

Plastic shrinkage may develop in the concrete during cold weather, especially if the air is dry or heat is used.

To avoid cold-weather problems, some builders stockpile foundations before cold weather starts, or they close in and heat basements before pouring basement slabs.

Curing

Curing is crucial to good concrete. Without a good cure, concrete dries out and may reach only 40 percent of its design strength.

Poorly cured concrete is more likely to crack and curl.

Poorly cured concrete does not wear well, is less watertight, does not stand up to freezing and thawing or deicers, tends to have more efflorescence, and is more likely to be discolored.

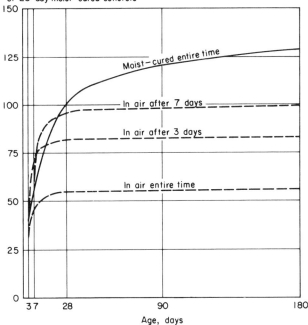

Compressive strength, per cent
of 28-day moist-cured concrete

- Moist-cured entire time
- In air after 7 days
- In air after 3 days
- In air entire time

Age, days

As the chart shows, concrete continues to gain strength as long as it is curing. However, note the brief surge in strength when the 3- and 7-day cures are stopped.

Curing occurs only with—
- Water
- A favorable temperature
- Time

Enough water for curing is already in the concrete no matter how low the water-cement ratio. Retaining this moisture is the most important part of curing, whatever the curing type used.

Normal air temperature supplies enough heat for curing. If people are comfortable, the concrete is comfortable and continues to cure. However, when the temperature drops curing slows. When the temperature is near freezing, curing almost stops. Therefore, curing procedures must continue much longer at low temperatures, unless special precautions are followed.

The basic cure takes a minimum of—
- 5 days at 70 degrees Fahrenheit or higher
- 7 days at 50 to 70 degrees Fahrenheit

Thin sections of concrete should cure longer. Cure longer also for more watertight concrete.

The lengths of time for basic cures are bare minimums. Cure longer in all cases whenever possible. The most important curing time is the first few days. Begin curing just as soon as the finishers get off the slab. Other points for good curing include—

- Taking special care with edges and joints where concrete is likely to fail first. Inadequate curing is also likely at these points.

- Remember that if the joints are to receive sealants, or a slab is to be covered with linoleum, tile, or carpet, the cure must leave a surface that can be bonded.
- Keep the cure as uniform as possible in moisture, heat, and length of time. The cure should be uniform all over—do not cure some parts longer than others. For example, when a polyethylene sheet used for curing is ripped or blown away from a slab edge, the curing will be uneven.

Do not let a wet-cured concrete surface dry too rapidly. Taper off the curing. The same rule applies if heat is used—lower the temperature gradually a few degrees per hour.

- After curing let the concrete surface air-dry a few days before using it, unless a curing compound is applied. With a curing compound the concrete can be used right after application. Always check manufacturers' recommendations.
- Longer air-drying is required if the concrete is air-entrained and is to be exposed to deicers; about 4 weeks are recommended. Curing compounds that do not allow air-drying should not be used when cold weather is approaching.

All types of cures keep the water in the concrete from escaping by either (a) sealing the surface without using water or (b) using water to seal the surface.

Curing Without Adding Water

Polyethylene Cure

For the polyethylene cure, wide sheets of polyethylene seal the surface. The sheets may be clear, white, or black. White is good in hot weather since it reflects light and heat. Black is good in cool weather for the opposite reason—it absorbs heat.

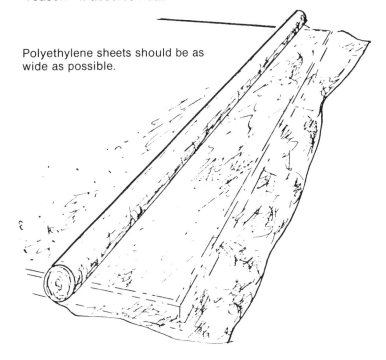

Polyethylene sheets should be as wide as possible.

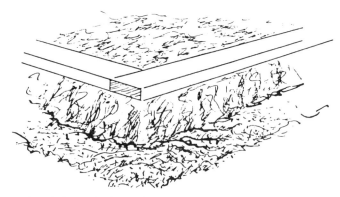

Carefully seal edges of polyethylene or water-proof paper and all joints with sand, tape, or mastic.

Wrinkles produce mottled discolored areas because of what is called the greenhouse effect.

Wetting the concrete before applying polyethylene is a good idea. The edges and laps of the sheets must be sealed because vapor pressure builds up underneath and must be contained for a good cure. The edges can be sealed with lumber and sand or earth. Joints can be sealed with sand, nonstaining mastic, or tape. Polyethylene sheets used for curing should be as wide as possible to avoid unnecessary laps.

Advantages and disadvantages. Polyethylene is easy to handle and place except in windy weather. It does not leave a film that will prevent bond with floor coverings, and it provides some protection against stains and debris. It is low cost, particularly if it is taken care of and reused, and it does not rot or mildew. It can be used for other purposes afterward, such as protecting lumber.

On the other hand, polyethylene that is placed in areas with a lot of activity can be punctured easily or the edges or laps can open. If this happens the cure will be uneven and stresses and cracking may result.

Sometimes polyethylene leaves a blotchy or mottled surface. This condition, called the greenhouse effect, is caused by water vapor condensing under wrinkles in the film and running down into puddles where the film is in contact with the slab. The damp spots change the color of the concrete slightly.

Because of the greenhouse effect and the potential discoloration, polyethylene curing is not recommended for colored concretes. Theoretically, if the film is perfectly flat, the greenhouse effect does not occur, but in

practice the film is almost certain to wrinkle.

Discoloration can be worse if calcium chloride is used and the surface is hard steel-troweled.

Waterproof Paper

The waterproof paper cure is quite similar to the polyethylene cure. Ordinary building paper should not be used; it may be water repellent but not vaporproof.

Curing paper must be vaporproof, strong, nonstaining, and nonshrinking. Good curing paper withstands some abuse and is reusable, although protecting it from construction traffic is a good idea.

Use wide sheets, seal all edges with sand or lumber, and seal laps with nonstaining mastic, glue, or tape. Keep the paper flat and wrinkle-free.

Wet the concrete thoroughly before placing the paper. Light-colored sheets are available for hot-weather curing and dark sheets for cool weather.

Advantages and disadvantages. Curing paper leaves the concrete surface clean and able to bond well with a floor covering. It gives some protection from stains and debris. Good curing paper usually has fewer wrinkles than the thinner, stretchable polyethylene and blotching from a greenhouse effect is less likely.

Liquid-Membrane-Curing Compounds

Among the many types of membrane cures, some only cure while others claim also to seal, harden, or dust-proof. These products may have a wax, resin, asphaltic, acrylic, epoxy, sodium silicate, rubber, or other base. Readers should check the nature of the compounds and read their labels carefully before using them. Membrane-curing compounds should meet the ASTM C156 and C309 standards.

The compound may seal the surface for a month or so and then gradually dissipate or wear off, depending on the type.

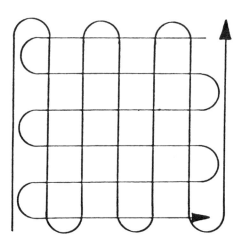

Spraying pattern

While curing goes on, traffic can proceed on the slab as soon as the compound hardens. The membrane should be covered and protected in heavy traffic areas to keep it from wearing off and creating a nonuniform cure with resultant cracks.

Good coverage is extremely important when curing compounds are used. Rather than make one heavy spraying pass, better coverage is obtained by making two lighter passes at right angles to each other.

A colored curing compound will allow missed spots to be seen right away. White, black, and grey liquid-membrane compounds are available. A fugitive dye can be added to clear compounds; and it will later virtually disappear.

Another way to check for coverage when using a clear liquid membrane is to cover a portion of the slab with polyethylene or waterproof paper. Check it later to see if moisture is accumulating under the covering. If it is, the membrane coverage is not good, nor is the cure.

Wax base, clear. A clear wax-base membrane curing compound is possibly the least expensive and is effective for about 28 days. Clear wax-base-membrane cures are not recommended if the concrete is to be painted, tiled, or treated, since the wax base leaves a slightly gummy residue that collects dirt. If a decision is made to paint a wax-cured surface, a wait of a year or more until it fully disintegrates may be necessary.

A fugitive dye that virtually disappears after a few days can be used to show coverage.

The wax cure was once quite popular but is no longer widely used.

Wax-resin base, clear. The wax-resin cure is one of the most commonly used today. It is typically less expensive than a resin cure. However, the waxy residue makes a poor surface for painting, tiling, or other surface treatment until it disintegrates. The length of time required for disintegration may be from 2 to 9 months, depending on the product. Painting over a wax-resin-base cure is not recommended until more than a year after the compound is applied, but again this depends on the product.

A fugitive dye can be used to show coverage.

Resin base, clear. The resin-base cure is also a popular cure. It may be more expensive than a wax-resin cure, but it has the advantage of allowing painting or other surface treatment, depending on the product. Some resin cures may not allow surface treatment until they disintegrate, in 30 to 60 days, or longer.

The resin cure's residual film is typically harder and more abrasion resistant than the wax cure and is less likely to wear off under traffic.

A fugitive dye can be used with resin-base cures.

White-pigmented cures. White-pigmented compounds may have wax or resin bases, but they are special formulations. Their advantage is their ability to lower heat buildup and evaporation in addition to indicating coverage.

White-pigmented cures often need to be stirred before using.

Black and grey compounds, complete or partial asphaltic base. Asphaltic-base compounds are usually relatively inexpensive. They are good waterproofers, especially when sandwiched between layers of a two-course slab. They can also be used on the slab surface and provide a good base for tile, linoleum, and other materials compatible with asphalt.

Black or grey compounds absorb heat from the sun, a virtue in cold weather.

Other membrane cures. Other membrane cures include chlorinated rubber, acrylics, epoxies, and sodium silicates. They may harden, dustproof, and seal against oil, depending on the product. Readers should check manufacturers' guidelines before using. Some experts do not recommend sodium silicate compounds.

Field tests show that synthetic-rubber-base compounds are far superior to resin-base compounds. The synthetic-rubber compounds may cost considerably more than resin cures but experts believe they provide a superior cure.

When to apply a curing compound. The best time to apply a typical curing compound is right after finishing. Do not apply it when the surface has standing water or is otherwise too wet. Applying a compound under wet conditions will produce a poor surface seal.

On the other hand, if the compound is applied when the concrete surface has dried out too much, the compound will be absorbed into the concrete and the surface seal will be poor. When the surface is dried out, fog the concrete to seal the pores before applying a membrane compound.

Some of the cures that claim to seal, harden, and dustproof are applied at a later time, for instance 8 hours after the concrete is finished. Check manufacturers' recommendations.

In any case, apply the membrane compound as soon as the application is allowed, before the concrete dries out too much.

Joints and membrane cures. If joints are to be sealed with a joint sealant, be sure that no adhesion problem will exist because of the curing compound used. Use a curing compound compatible with the sealant, or cover the joints before applying the compound so that it cannot get inside them. If the compound is omitted at the joints, they must be cured in some other way.

Deicers and membrane cures. If concrete is placed in the fall and it is expected to be exposed soon to freeze-thaw or deicers, a membrane cure may not be recommended since recently applied membrane compounds do not allow the 4 weeks of air drying needed before subjection to freeze-thaw or deicers.

Advantages and disadvantages of membrane-compound curing. Membrane compounds are simple to apply, inexpensive for both labor and materials, and typically allow construction activity to proceed soon afterward. A cure is reliable if it meets ASTM C 156 and C 309 requirements and if it is applied properly and protected when necessary.

White compounds are available that lessen heat and evaporation in hot weather. Black or grey asphaltic curing compounds help warm the concrete in cool weather and are good waterproofers, especially for two-layer slabs. They also provide good adhesion for materials bonded with asphaltic adhesives.

Coverage can be a problem if clear membrane cures are used. If the coverage is poor, curing will be poor. For this reason pigmented cures are advised. Fugitive dyes that later virtually disappear are available for clear compounds. Two thin applications at right angles to each other are recommended for good coverage.

Painting, sealants for joints, and other surface coatings can be a problem with membrane compounds. Wax-type compounds make adhesion particularly difficult. Check the compound for compatibility with any surface coating.

Deicers can cause problems for membrane-cured concrete if the curing takes place late in the fall. The curing material may not have a chance to disintegrate and allow the 4 weeks of air-drying needed before exposure to deicers.

Always check manufacturers' recommendations before using membrane cures.

Curing by Adding Water

Generally, curing with water is effective if it is done properly. The basic problem with wet curing is keeping the concrete continuously and uniformly wet. In some cases an unreliable cure is worse than no cure at all.

Wet cures should be tapered off gradually. The concrete should air-dry for a few days before use and for 4 weeks if it is to be exposed to freeze-thaw or deicers.

Wet Burlap

The proper burlap for wet curing is a specially treated material available in rolls. It is fireproof and rot-resistant and does not discolor or otherwise harm the concrete. Some burlaps are coated with plastic or aluminum to reflect light and heat.

The specially treated burlap is spread over the concrete and kept continuously and uniformly wet during the basic curing period. It must not be allowed to dry out. If it does, it may actually draw water from the concrete and that will be worse than no cure at all.

Advantages and disadvantages of wet burlap. Wet burlap is a very effective cure if it is done properly. It does not mottle or discolor the concrete surface, and it leaves a clean surface that can be painted or otherwise coated. Good burlap is economical and reusable.

Perhaps the wet burlap's greatest disadvantage is the need to ensure that it stay continuously wet. An automatic system may break down and manpower may not always wet the burlap on time. Besides, the cost of labor and equipment to do the wetting must be added to the overall cost.

Another disadvantage is that activity on the slab may have to be restricted during the cure.

Sprinkling or Fogging

A mechanical arrangement of pipes or hoses with sprinklers is stretched across or around the concrete when a sprinkling or fogging cure is used. The system may turn on automatically or be turned on by hand at set intervals.

The water may run off or evaporate more rapidly during hot, dry, or windy weather, and therefore the intervals between sprinkling will vary. If the surface dries between sprinklings, crazing or cracking can result.

Advantages and disadvantages of sprinkling or fogging. Like the wet-burlap cure, sprinkling or fogging is a good cure if done properly. It does not mottle or discolor the surface if it does not dry out in spots. It leaves a clean surface suitable for painting or other coatings.

A sprinkling or fogging cure may be relatively costly in equipment, labor, and supervision. Possibly a greater disadvantage is maintaining quality control. The equipment may break down, the pipes may leak, the nozzles may clog, or the wind may blow and make some areas difficult to dampen. Low humidity, heat, and wind affect the evaporation rate, and dry spots may occur suddenly. Also, activity on the slab is impossible during curing.

Ponding

Ponding is probably the best curing method for quality concrete.

Some sort of barrier such as a wooden frame must be placed around the concrete to contain the curing water, which may be several inches deep.

When the curing period is over and the pond is drained, the surface should be sprayed or fogged occasionally for a day or two, tapering off gradually.

Ponding is not often used in residential concreting. Possibly it is thought to be too troublesome or too costly to supervise. These criticisms are often not justified. In fact, ponding can be both effective and economical. The areas to be cured in residential concreting are small, and sometimes they need little in the way of dams. If the system is designed properly, little supervision is needed.

Advantages and disadvantages of ponding. Ponding may be the best cure for strong, watertight concrete. It is economical and requires little supervision if done correctly. It leaves a clean surface suitable for painting or any type of covering.

Ponding has an unusual advantage: The water serves as a buffer or insulator against the environment and keeps the concrete at a more constant temperature regardless of exterior heat, cold, humidity, or wind.

One disadvantage is that activity on the slab is halted during the cure.

Quality control can be a problem, though probably not as much as with wet burlap and sprinkling cures. The damming system could break and the water be lost. Leaks around the edges of the dam could affect a poorly prepared subgrade. These problems can be avoided with good construction practices.

As with all cures, a supervisor should check regularly to see that no problems develop.

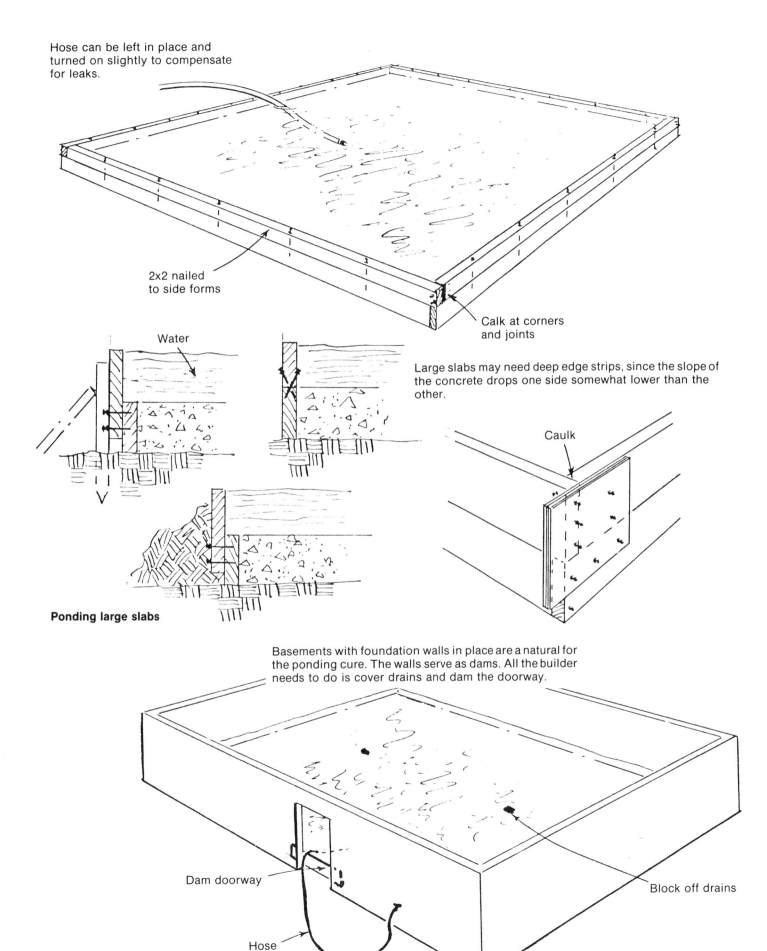

Hose can be left in place and turned on slightly to compensate for leaks.

2x2 nailed to side forms

Calk at corners and joints

Water

Large slabs may need deep edge strips, since the slope of the concrete drops one side somewhat lower than the other.

Caulk

Ponding large slabs

Basements with foundation walls in place are a natural for the ponding cure. The walls serve as dams. All the builder needs to do is cover drains and dam the doorway.

Dam doorway

Block off drains

Hose

49

Curing in Hot, Dry, or Windy Weather

Special curing is only one of many measures needed in hot, dry, or windy weather. Other measures relate to subgrade preparations, mix design, cooling, and evaporation control.

Beginning the cure immediately after finishing—although always important—is especially important in hot, dry, or windy weather. Measures to retain moisture in the concrete can be started during the finishing operation by using wet burlap, polyethylene covers, shades, and windbreaks.

A properly managed wet cure helps cool the concrete in hot, dry weather.

Ponding may be best in hot, dry weather. It is not only an effective cure, but the water also serves as a buffer, keeping the concrete cool and at a more uniform temperature. Ponding may be more reliable than other methods—less likely to break down or slip in quality.

No matter what type of cure is used in hot, dry, or windy weather, quality control is extremely important. Heat and rapid evaporation will encourage stresses and cracks unless moisture is retained with good curing techniques.

Cures that do not require additional water—such as polyethylene sheets, waterproof paper, or a liquid membrane—may be chosen because traffic is necessary on the slab during curing or because such a cure is more economical under the particular circumstances. When these cures are used, the slab should be dampened before curing is begun.

Whenever possible, use a white-tinted curing material to help control heat buildup and evaporation.

With polyethylene or paper cures, special care is needed to properly seal all laps and edges. This is particularly important because of evaporation in hot, dry, or windy weather.

Wrinkles in the polyethylene sheets may be more likely to cause mottling from the greenhouse effect in hot, dry weather.

In all cases, but particularly in wet curing and more particularly in hot, dry, or windy weather, the cure should be tapered off.

Curing in Cold Weather

Cold weather requires special curing procedures and also special attention to subgrade preparation, mix design, protection, admixtures such as calcium chloride, and special finishing precautions. (See the sections "The Subgrade in Cold Weather," "Admixtures," and "Placing and Finishing in Cold Weather" in this book.)

If concrete freezes before curing is completed, it can be permanently damaged. Resuming proper curing after concrete has frozen may help restore some of its desirable properties, but it will not restore all.

Faster curing can often save the concrete as well as save time. Use of high-early-strength cement is one way of accelerating hydration and thus curing; the addi-

tion of calcium chloride in the mix is another. Heating the ingredients will briefly speed up hydration.

More important are measures to keep the concrete warm for at least several days after finishing. This greatly increases the rate of strength gain.

The concrete itself supplies some heat for curing even in cold weather—if the heat is trapped in the concrete with an insulating material. Special blankets or two layers of polyethylene film or waterproof paper with straw between the layers are good insulators.

The edges of the insulating material must be firmly held down to keep the cure uniform so that cracking stresses will not develop from variations in temperature and moisture.

Very cold weather may require additional heat for the concrete. Do not use oil or gas heaters or any type of heater that gives off exhaust fumes unless the exhaust is vented to the outside. Carbon dioxide may cause the concrete to dust, and carbon monoxide may harm or kill people who breathe it.

The heat must be evenly dispersed to avoid cracking, crazing, or dusting. Heated air is low in humidity, so the concrete surface should be wetted.

After the cure, lower the heat gradually several degrees per hour, so that the concrete is not shocked into cracking. The concrete's temperature should not drop more than 40 degrees Fahrenheit in 24 hours.

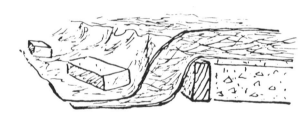

When insulating green concrete use bricks or lumber to hold down layered edges of polyethylene sheets that have straw sandwiched between the layers.

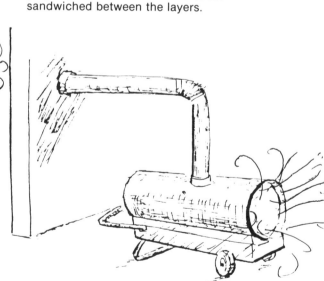

Vent heater exhausts to the outside to avoid harming concrete or workers.

Part 3. CONCRETE PROBLEMS

Some of the more typical onsite problems, their causes, and measures to prevent them are covered here. Other problems may relate to type of aggregate, other mix materials, and soil conditions.*

Crazing, Dusting, Scaling

Crazing, dusting, and scaling each has its unique cause, but each also shares a common cause—finishing when bleed water is on the surface.

Bullfloating and hand or machine floating and troweling while bleed water is present cause the sand and cement to work to the surface and mix with the bleed

Dusting. Fine dust that rubs off on finger. Is not necessarily a sign of serious deterioration.

Crazing. A network of fine surface cracks. May collect dust and moisture. Not as serious as scaling. Does not necessarily seriously affect concrete quality.

water. The result is a sandy, high-water-cement-ratio mix at the surface—a perfect recipe for a weak, crack-prone surface. The result can be crazing, dusting, scaling, or even delaminating of the surface.

Sprinkling water or cement on the surface to make

finishing easier will have the same effect and should be prohibited.

In some special cases, such as in very hot, dry, windy weather, evaporation is so rapid that a fine water spray has been used during finishing to prevent plastic shrinkage cracks. However, this technique is questionable and other techniques that accomplish the same goal should be looked into.

Using too wet a mix to start with contributes to the bleeding and the crazing, dusting, and scaling. Poor curing worsens these problems.

---

*If the cause of a concrete problem is not clear, write to or call:

National Association of Home Builders
Technical Services Department
15th and M Streets, N.W.
Washington, D.C. 20005
(202) 822-0300

National Ready Mixed Concrete Association
900 Spring Street
Silver Spring, Maryland 20910
(301) 587-1400

Air-entrainment, on the other hand, lessens bleeding and thereby helps prevent crazing, dusting, and scaling.

Crazing can be caused by low humidity, rapid surface drying, or too much cement in the mix. Excessive cement generates greater stress when the concrete sets up and is another reason why cement should not be used to absorb excess surface water during finishing.

Dusting is sometimes caused by carbon dioxide gas from unvented heaters. The carbon monoxide from use of such heaters in an enclosed space is also dangerous to workers and can cause death.

Dry heat even without exhaust gases also causes dusting.

A mix that is rich in sand and low in cement causes dusting.

Certain chemical surface treatments help harden a surface damaged by dusting. If the dusting is only a surface problem, the concrete can be ground down to stronger concrete.

Scaling is sometimes caused by freeze-thaw cycles and deicers. Scaling can happen even in enclosed areas such as garages if deicer drippings get in the concrete. Sometimes damage from freeze-thaw and deicers is so great that the concrete spalls. Therefore, concrete should be protected against freeze-thaw or deicers. (See the section "Scaling and Spalling, Freeze-Thaw, and Deicers" following.)

permitted to bring the load to the specified slump.) Increasing the water-cement ratio will seriously affect the strength of the concrete and other desirable properties.

- Make sure that good finishing practices are followed—the most important practice is not to work the concrete when bleed water is present. (See "Finishing the Concrete" starting on page 39.)
- Finally, make sure that good curing practices are followed. Ponding is probably the best method. Allow enough air-drying time before deicers are applied. Four weeks of air-drying the concrete after curing are recommended.

Spalling

The spalling referred to in this manual is a deeper weakness than surface scaling, although the two terms are sometimes used interchangeably. When the concrete spalls, a large chunk breaks off, showing a weakness that may extend to the full depth of a slab. The immediate cause of the spall may be a blow or exposure to freezing and thawing; or a chunk of concrete may break off at a slab edge or joint for no apparent reason.

Scaling. A serious problem. Surface scales off, leaving a roughened irregular surface. May lead to other problems. May be a particular problem on driveways.

Spalling. A deeper weakness than scaling with larger chunks breaking off.

Good concrete must have a low water-cement ratio, have other materials in the correct proportions, and be properly cured and air-dried so that it can resist scaling and spalling.

Measures to prevent scaling include—

- Use a reliable ready mix supplier. The supplier has much to do with the quality of the mix and its resistance to scaling. Unsound aggregates can cause popouts leading to scaling. The sand should not have too much fine material; the concrete must be mixed thoroughly to get good air-entrainment; the percent of air entrained must be correct; and the mix must have a slump that is not too high.
- After the concrete has been delivered make sure that no more water is added to increase the slump. (Upon arrival at the jobsite, one addition of water is

The way to prevent spalling—regardless of the immediate cause—is to use spall-resistant concrete. Spall-resistant concrete is also crack- and scale-resistant and watertight.

Follow the rules for good concrete:

- Use a good mix with a low water-cement ratio. If too much of any ingredient is used—sand, cement, or water—the concrete either will be weak or stresses will be created that lead to cracking and spalling. The wrong type of ingredients also cause spalling.
- Water-reducing admixtures (plasticizers) allow a reduction in the water and still produce workable concrete.
- Air entrainment for concrete exposed to freeze-thaw or deicers helps it absorb the freeze-thaw stresses.

- Properly finished concrete usually affects surface phenomena such as scaling more than it affects deeper spalling, but the two conditions overlap somewhat. Most importantly, do not finish with bleed water on the surface and do not add water, cement, or sand to the surface to ease finishing.
- Curing properly may be the single most important factor for resistance to spalling, or it at least shares equal importance with a low water-cement ratio.

Good curing greatly increases the strength of concrete—in fact, it may more than double the strength.

Curing may be poorest at those points most likely to spall—the edges and joints. If the edges and joints are poorly cured and the rest of the concrete is properly cured, the edges and joints will not only be weak, but the difference in curing may actually set up stresses that will cause cracks and spalling.

Other causes of spalling, such as corrosion of embedded metals and aggregate reactions, can be impeded by good curing.

Scaling and Spalling, Freeze-Thaw, and Deicers

Concrete is especially prone to scale or spall if it is exposed to ice and freeze-thaw cycles, particularly if deicer salts are used.

The following general guidelines can be used to make concrete more resistant to freeze-thaw and deicers:

- Make good, strong concrete. The water-cement ratio should not exceed 0.5 and the slump should be between 3 and 5 inches, depending on how it is to be placed. A water-reducing plasticizer allows less water usage. Use at least 6 bags of cement per cubic yard of concrete and sound, well-graded aggregate. Place and finish properly.
- Air entrainment is essential for freeze-thaw and deicer resistance. The amount varies with air temperature and admixtures. The amount and quality should be well monitored.
- Cure the concrete properly. Curing may need to be longer than ordinary in cool weather. If a normal Type I cement is used, 7 days of curing at 70 degrees Fahrenheit are recommended for extra protection.
- Air-dry the concrete. Air-entrained concrete should be air-dried for 4 weeks after curing to increase its resistance to deicers. Liquid-membrane cures applied in late fall may not allow sufficient time for air-drying before exposure to freeze-thaw or deicers, so another type cure is recommended.
- Apply a surface treatment to help protect the concrete against deicers and lessen scaling and spalling, particularly if the air-drying period is cut short.

Boiled linseed oil or neutral petroleum oil can be used as a surface treatment. The surface should be clean and dry before applying. Make two applications of the oil. Mix the first application with an equal part of solvent such as turpentine, naphtha, or mineral spirits. The second application can be pure linseed oil.

The neutral petroleum oil should be mixed with an equal part of a solvent such as Stoddard's. Both surface treatments may need to be repeated in future years.

Some authorities highly recommend linseed oil emulsion as both a cure and a scaling-spalling preventative. The emulsion is not the same as the linseed oil in solvent described here.

Cracks

Concrete shrinks as it hardens. If it is restrained from moving, the resulting shrinkage stresses will be relieved by cracks.

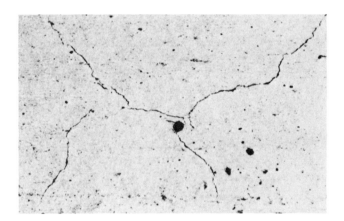

Cracking.

The builder cannot hope to avoid cracks totally. However, controlling the cracks is possible. The guidelines for controlling cracking are much the same as those for making concrete spall-resistant:

- A low water-cement ratio is possibly the most important factor. The more water that is used in the mix the weaker the concrete will be, with less strength to resist cracks.
- Good curing helps concrete gain strength before shrinkage stresses develop. With good curing the ultimate strength is high and the ultimate stress is low.
- Keeping the concrete temperature uniform during curing helps prevent cracks. Avoid sudden temperature changes or abrupt termination of curing; make the cure uniform.
- The subgrade too must be firm and uniform.
- Do not restrain the concrete. Use isolation joints at foundation walls and around columns. (See the sections "Controlling Cracking" on page 7 and "Isolation Joints" on page 27.)

- Control where cracks may occur by—
  1. Making joints. To be effective control joints should be one fourth the slab depth (see the section "Locating Control Joints").
  2. Add wire mesh or reinforcing steel bars to the concrete. The reinforcement reduces the size of the cracks, distributes them uniformly, and keeps the aggregate interlocked at cracks to reduce displacement. (See "Installing Reinforcement" on page 36.)

Plastic-Shrinkage Cracks

Plastic-shrinkage cracks usually form when the concrete is still plastic or not completely hardened. They are typically caused by rapid evaporation, when the water leaves the surface faster than it is replaced by bleeding.

Plastic shrinkage cracks.

Plastic-shrinkage cracks are more likely to occur in hot, dry, windy weather. However, they may occur in cool weather if evaporation is very rapid because of high winds, low humidity, or concentrated artificial heat. Very warm concrete in cold surrounding air may cause evaporation and plastic-shrinkage cracks.

Plastic-shrinkage cracks can be prevented by using these techniques:

- Slow evaporation is recommended. Use windbreaks, temporary covers, or shades; cool the concrete or place it in the cool part of the day. Begin the cure immediately after finishing or even before finishing by covering the concrete with wet burlap or polyethylene film.

  Sometimes a fine spray or a fog nozzle is used to keep the surface damp, but it is not recommended. Water builds up on the surface when fogging. Water worked into the surface during finishing is a main cause of crazing, dusting, and scaling.

- Increase bleeding. Avoid high cement or sand con-

tent. Use as much water as possible without harming strength; dampen subgrade, forms, and aggregates; use tools that encourage bleeding, such as wood floats instead of magnesium floats.

- Hold water in dispersion in the concrete longer to decrease the moisture difference between surface and interior. Use air entrainment or increase the fineness of the sand.

If plastic-shrinkage cracks begin to form during finishing, tamp on both sides with a float to bring the crack together and then refloat.

Blisters

Blisters range from ¼ inch to 4 inches in diameter and they are about ⅛ inch deep. They appear when the concrete surface is sealed while air or water is still rising to the surface.

The following general rules help prevent blisters:

- Do not work the concrete too much. Overworking it may cause aggregate to settle and bleed water to rise.
- Do not seal the surface too soon. Use a wood bullfloat on non-air-entrained concrete to avoid sealing the surface.

Use only magnesium or aluminum tools on air-entrained concrete. Air-entrained concrete is not as likely to blister since less bleed water is present.

The following rules for avoiding blisters are provided by Carl Peterson, a master cement mason and instructor from Lenexa, Kansas:

- Warm the subgrade in cold weather.
- Use a proper mix of 5½ to 6 bags of cement with no excessive fines.
- Avoid using water-reducing admixtures if problems result.
- Important: do not overwork concrete with tools such as vibrating screeds, jitterbugs, or bullfloats; use these tools as little as possible.
- When the concrete is air-entrained, timing is often misjudged. Before hand-floating, an adult's weight should not make a footprint in the concrete deeper than ¼ inch; before machine-floating, the footprint should not be deeper than ⅛ inch.
- Hand magnesium floats are recommended where deficient surface moisture is a problem.
- Flat floating and troweling are recommended.
- Proper timing with an adequate delay between passes is important.
- On windy days a fog spray or slab cover can be used. Maximum volume of water from fog-spray nozzle should be ½ gallon of water per minute.

If blisters begin forming on the concrete, a slight fog spray followed by a wood float in a swirly pattern may help; flatten the trowel. The next troweling may need to be delayed.

Bugholes

Bugholes, sometimes called blow holes, are small cavities that appear because of air bubbles trapped in the surface of vertically formed concrete. They can be reduced by adjusting the sand content of the mix and by proper vibration, and corrected by sacking or rubbing.

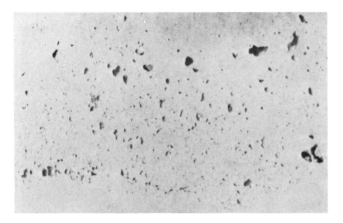

Bugholes.

Pitting

Small cavities called pitting develop from corrosion and disintegration on the concrete surface. Good curing can help prevent pitting. The damage can be corrected by sacking or rubbing.

Popouts

Popouts are shallow, conical sections that break away from the surface of concrete. They occur when aggregates split or expand near the surface of the concrete, creating internal pressure that causes a piece of the concrete to pop out. Another cause is alkali-silica reaction. Use of good-quality aggregate will avoid popouts.

Popouts.

Curling

Curling occurs when the slab rises slightly at the corners and edges. It happens when the top of the slab shrinks more or faster than the bottom.

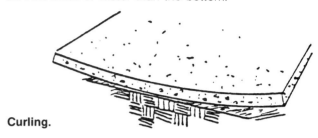

Curling.

The most likely reason is too much variation in moisture or temperature between the top and the bottom. With good curing, concrete will not curl because the concrete has been kept uniform in moisture and temperature from top to bottom.

Other factors that may contribute to curling include slabs that are too thin and control joints that are too far apart.

The remedy for curling is water curing, such as ponding, until the concrete flattens as much as possible. Then the concrete should be cut into smaller squares.

Blowups

A blowup is the buckling upward of concrete on both sides of a joint or crack. Blowups occur usually in hot weather when the joints do not absorb the expanded concrete, because they are too narrow, too far apart, or filled with incompressible material such as sand or gravel.

Blowup.

Efflorescence

Efflorescence is a crystalline deposit of soluble salts, usually white, that forms on the surface of masonry or concrete. It is generally harmless.

Three conditions are needed for efflorescence to occur: (1) soluble salts must be present, (2) moisture must be present to pick up the salts, and (3) evaporation or hydrostatic pressure must cause the solution to move.

The best way to prevent efflorescence is to make good watertight concrete with a low water-cement ratio, properly graded aggregate, the right amount of cement, air entrainment, well-consolidated placement, and good curing.

Vapor barriers on exterior walls and below the slab may help prevent efflorescence.

To remove efflorescence, dry-brush or lightly sandblast the concrete and then flush the surface with water.

If this treatment does not work, a 5 to 10 percent solution of muriatic acid may help. Be safe and wear gloves and goggles when working with acid. For integrally colored concrete, a more dilute mix of about 2 percent should be used to prevent etching that may affect appearance. Before using the acid dampen the entire surface. Dampen small areas at a time, but dampen the entire surface. Flush with water afterward.

An alternative is to use a 1 to 3 percent phosphoric or acetic acid solution.

Discoloration

Concrete may appear lighter, darker, mottled, or otherwise discolored in random spots. Though many factors cause discoloration, possibly the most important cause is lack of uniformity in the mix or in the cure. The most significant lack of uniformity may be the amount of water in the mixture.

If the water-cement ratio varies, the concrete's color will vary. If curing does not provide the same amount of water on all of the concrete, the color may vary. A cure with polyethylene or curing paper will produce a greenhouse effect where moisture condenses under wrinkles and runs down, spotting the surface where the water puddles.

Discoloration.

If the subgrade is not uniformly damp, the concrete can discolor.

Everything in the concrete mixture should be uniform. Do not order ready mixed concrete for the same job from different plants. Schedule the job so that the mix design, placing, finishing, and curing do not vary.

Other causes of discoloration include calcium chloride added to the mix (especially if more than 2 percent of weight of cement is used) and hard-steel troweling for too long (particularly if calcium chloride is used).[*] To remove discoloration of these types, washdowns with water may be helpful. Stainless steel or plastic trowels are used sometimes on white concrete to help avoid discoloration. Dusting wet concrete with cement to ease finishing can cause discoloration as well as crazing, dusting, and other surface problems.

Removing other discoloration such as ink, oil, urine, or tobacco will need special techniques.[**]

Flash Set

Flash set occurs when the concrete sets rapidly before it can be finished. Flash set can be caused by adding hot water of 140 degrees Fahrenheit or more directly to the concrete, using too much calcium chloride or other accelerators, or a combination of factors. Flash set may happen in cold or hot weather.

Cold Joint

A cold joint is a weak bond that forms when one batch of concrete sets up before the next batch is placed against it.

To avoid cold joints, place each new batch against the preceding batch without too much time between pours. Do not dump the concrete in separate piles.

Dished Surface or High Edges

A dished surface can result from finishing concrete that is low in the forms. Even if the concrete is struck off level with the forms, some shrinkage will occur, especially if too much water is used.

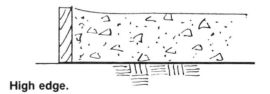

High edge.

---

[*]See *Surface Discoloration of Concrete Flatwork*, Research Bulletin RX203, Portland Cement Association, Skokie, Illinois, 1966.
[**]See *Removing Stains and Cleaning Concrete Surfaces*, IS214T, Portland Cement Association, Skokie, Illinois, 1981.

To prevent dished surfaces:

- Strike off the concrete a bit higher than the side forms to allow for shrinkage.
- After floating, use the back of the trowel to straighten the edge and then finish the slab.
- Place a thin strip of wood on the top of the form and remove it after the first floating and troweling. The strip will leave the concrete a bit high, and let the power float and trowel extend 4 to 6 inches past the edge. This step helps keep the edge in line and prevent dishing.

Dished surfaces may also result from faulty bullfloating. As the mason pushes the bullfloat across the slab and then prepares to return, the bullfloat may dig in slightly. To prevent this, gently jiggle the bullfloat to loosen it before returning. Bullfloating a second time in a perpendicular direction or darbying the surface in addition to bullfloating may help.

Patching and Repairing

Regardless of whether the repair to be made is a spall, crack, or large resurfacing or whether the patching material is concrete, epoxy, epoxy mortar, or latex concrete, there are two essentials for a good repair:

1. The area to be repaired must be clean, rough, and sound.
2. The patching material must be designed for minimal shrinkage.

Patching Spalled Areas with Concrete

Saw or chisel the edges of the spalled area as shown; angle the cuts toward the undamaged concrete.

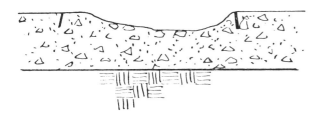

Chip out the area between. Leave the chipped area rough and make sure that the concrete is firm and sound.

Use an airblast or vacuum to clean the hole thoroughly. Then fill the hole with water and let it stand for at least an hour.

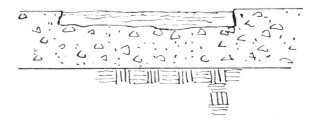

Some experts disagree on the wetting procedure. They maintain that the grout may bond better without thorough wetting of the concrete.

Prepare a grout mix of 1 part portland cement, 1 to 2 parts fine sand, and enough water for a creamy mix.

Remove any water left in the hole after it has soaked for at least an hour. The concrete should be damp with no standing water.

Brush the grout over the entire area to be patched, including the sides of the hole.

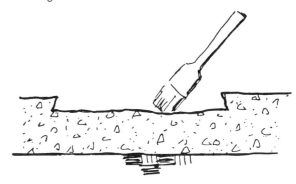

Make up a batch of concrete that is the same as the original concrete, except that—

- The slump should be zero. In other words the mix should be earth-dry or just wet enough to be worked into a ball by hand pressure.
- The aggregate size should not exceed half of the patch depth. If possible, use concrete sand rather than mortar sand.
- Since the patch mix is likely to be darker than the surrounding concrete, white cement can be used in place of some grey portland cement. If time permits, experiment to determine how much white cement is needed. Typically, about one-fourth white cement is a good mix.

After mixing, let stand for 15 to 30 minutes to minimize shrinkage before putting it in the hole.

Place the patch mix in the hole and compact it, overfilling slightly. In deep holes, pack the mix in 1-inch layers. Finish with a float and trowel. Cure for at least 3 days, or longer if possible. A water cure is recommended.

To make a good patch remember that—

- Patch shrinkage can be a problem. Using zero-slump concrete and a good cure will help.
- The surface should be roughened. Using acid is dangerous. An air hammer or a scarifying machine is recommended. Sandblasting is all right provided it roughens the surface.
- The surface to be patched must be clean and free of dust, debris, oil, and other foreign matter.
- If the old concrete contains reinforcing bars and the patch is as deep as the bars, place the patching material about ¾ inch around the bars.
- If the patched area is over a joint, the patch must be jointed directly over the original joint.

When patching cracks, follow the same procedure used for patching spalled areas. The crack should be cut out in the same way or routed out and thoroughly cleaned.

Patching Spalled Areas with Epoxy

Epoxy products vary by manufacturer; therefore the manufacturer's recommendations should always be checked before using. The following comments are meant only to give a general idea of how to use typical epoxies:

Before patching with epoxy, the surface to be patched should be—

- Sound, clean, and slightly roughened.
- Dry or basically dry with no water vapor moving up through the concrete. Special epoxies are available for damp concrete.
- At the proper temperature, usually between 60 and 100 degrees Fahrenheit. Special epoxies are available for temperatures below 40 degrees Fahrenheit and for the 40- to 60-degree range. Heating the epoxy speeds up hardening. Leaving it in the mixing pot builds up heat and speeds hardening. At low temperatures the concrete may need to be heated to at least a 3-inch depth to accelerate hardening.

Sand—and sometimes a larger aggregate—is generally added to the epoxy before patching, because epoxy and concrete have different expansion-contraction factors. Adding aggregate helps make the epoxy's expansion and contraction more like concrete. If aggregate is not used, the epoxy patch tends to break loose from the concrete. Only sand is added to thin patches. Sand and coarse aggregate are added to thicker patches, but the aggregate size should not exceed one third the patch thickness.

Remember that different epoxies are used for different situations such as indoor or outdoor patching, high- or low-bonding temperatures, and patching new concrete to old.

Making an Epoxy-Mortar Patch

When patching with epoxy, vertical or sloping cuts at the spall edges are not necessary. Roughen slightly the area to be patched for at least 12 inches beyond the

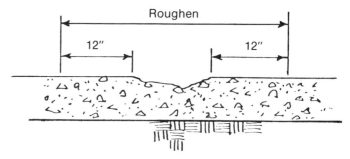

spall. Clean the concrete surface of all oil, grease, and loose concrete. Chipping and sandblasting the surface are recommended.

Dry the surface unless a special epoxy is to be used. Be sure no moisture is rising through the concrete.

The concrete and air should be in the right temperature range, usually 60 to 100 degrees Fahrenheit unless special epoxies are used. The concrete should be heated if necessary.

Prime the roughened and cleaned concrete with epoxy. If the spall has steep sides or reinforcing steel, the mix might need short fibers or a thixotropic agent to prevent runoff. Check the manufacturer's recommendations before using.

Add aggregate to the epoxy to make epoxy mortar. Use sand alone for patches that are no deeper than ¾ inch—that is, concrete sand with a range of particle sizes rather than mortar sand with more uniform particles. Use coarse aggregate with the sand for patches deeper than ¾ inch. The aggregate should be no larger that one-third the patch depth. The epoxy binder-aggregate ratio by weight is generally in the 1:7 to 1:10 range, depending on the maximum size of the aggregate.

Apply the epoxy mortar to the patch area, featheredging where necessary. The mortar should be applied before the epoxy primer hardens to avoid having to sandblast the primer before adding mortar. If the patch is more than 5 inches deep, build it up in two or more layers to prevent low spots and reduce heat buildup and subsequent contraction. Entrapped air reduces epoxy's strength and increases the coefficient of thermal expansion, so stir the mortar to release it.

Finish the patch with a trowel.

Finally, broadcast a light layer of sand over the patch and the surrounding primed area, till it has a uniform appearance.

When patching a spalled joint with epoxy mortar, be sure the joint is clean and roughened. A steel plate or trowel can be used as backstop. Remove the backstop after striking off the mortar.

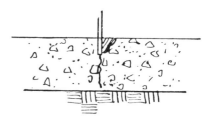

Additional Uses for Epoxy

- Epoxy coatings with mineral particles can be used for skid-resistant surfaces.
- Epoxy can be pumped into cracks to seal them, but check the manufacturer's recommendations first.
- Concrete can be coated with epoxy for greater resistance to deicers, moisture, and wear.
- Epoxies can be used to bond fresh concrete to old concrete, or old concrete to old concrete if a chunk breaks off (see manufacturer's recommendations). Special epoxy is needed to bond fresh concrete to old. A special epoxy may be needed for bonding old concrete to old concrete in some cases (for example, in bonding horizontal surfaces).

In all uses of epoxy be sure to follow manufacturer's recommendations for safety and for cleaning tools.

Patching Spalled Areas with Latex Mortar

As with the epoxies, different latexes are used for different conditions. Check manufacturer's recommendations before using latex products.

Latex modifiers in ordinary mortar provide good adhesion, resilience, elasticity, and durability. They can be used for both interior and exterior patching.

Latex can be applied to the base concrete, and then ordinary concrete patching mortar can be used for the patch. Latex also can be mixed with the water for the patching concrete, making a latex mortar.

Some general notes on using latex:

- Latex-modified mortar turns a green color during the initial cure; but the concrete will be a normal grey color after it is cured.
- Latex mortar has a high slump of up to 8 or 10 inches.
- Latex mortar should not be air-entrained because it loses stability with air entrainment.
- It should be applied on a damp base and must be struck off and finished rapidly because of its short working life.
- Since latex mortar clings tenaciously to tools, rapid cleanup of equipment is essential.

Other Patching Agents

Various resins, resinous emulsions, acrylics, and polymers are also used as bonding agents for concrete patches. Characteristics vary with the product and the manufacturer.

Resurfacing Slabs*

A topping may be either bonded to the base slab or unbonded. The topping and base slab should either operate as a unit or be totally independent. The choice of whether to bond or not to bond influences how the topping is constructed, including control joints.

Do no bond the topping if the base slab has structural movement or serious cracking.

Bond the topping if the base slab is basically sound. Topping depth should be a minimum of ¾ inch for bonded slabs, and a minimum of 3 inches for unbonded slabs.

Applying a Bonded Topping

Follow the general rules given for patching. Surface preparation is extremely important: The concrete should be clean and roughened. Use a low water-cement ratio to give low shrinkage, high strength, and good bond.

Roughen the surface with a scarifying machine, a jackhammer, or a chipping or rough-grinding tool. The surface does not need to be extremely rough, but should be slightly roughened all over. If the roughening operation goes beyond a reinforcing bar, roughen a minimum of ¾ inch around the bar.

Clean the surface with a vacuum or its equivalent, wash with water, brush, and reinspect. If acid is used to roughen the surface, use litmus paper to ensure that all the acid has been flushed away.

Dampen the concrete surface before the grout is brushed into place, particularly if the temperature is 60 degrees Fahrenheit or better. But there should be *no standing water* when the grout is placed. Ideally the base concrete should be dampened several hours ahead of time.

Apply a 1/16- to ⅛-inch-thick layer of bonding grout just before the resurfacing concrete is placed. This grout should be 1 part portland cement, 1 part fine concrete sand, and ½ part water. Mix the grout to a thick creamy consistency and broom it onto the surface. In no case should the grout dry before the topping is placed.

The concrete topping should contain pea gravel, crushed stone, or other suitable coarse aggregate graded up to a top size of ⅜ inch and well-graded concrete sand. The aggregate should be no larger than half the topping thickness. A mix of 1 part portland cement, 1 part sand, and 1½ to 2 parts coarse material is recommended. Use as little mixing water as possible. A water-cement ratio should be no more than 0.44, or 5 gallons of water per 94-pound bag of cement, including any free water in the sand. The slump should be near zero. Special equipment such as vibratory screeds, tampers, or power disk floats may be needed to place and compact the concrete.

This type of low-slump topping probably should be mixed on the job. Ready mix companies may have difficulty controlling such a mix.

Strike off about ⅜ inch high.

Finish the concrete by power floating because it compacts such a dry mix better than hand floating.

---

*For further information on topping slabs, see *Resurfacing Concrete Floors*, IS144T, Portland Cement Association, Skokie, Illinois, 1981

Control joints for a bonded topping slab should be exactly over the joints in the base slab, at least as wide as the base joints, and extend completely through the topping.

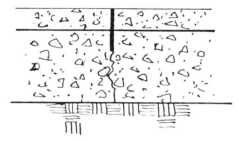

Control joints for bonded toppings

Joints can be formed by inserting strips in the base joints to serve as fillers for the topping-slab joints; or the joints can be sawn out and filled with a sealer.

Curing is even more important in bonded resurfacing than in ordinary concrete work, particularly in hot, dry, windy weather. Good curing is essential not only because of topping-slab thinness, but also for shrinkage-stress control and a good bond with the base slab.

Wet curing by ponding is recommended.

- Start as soon as possible.
- Cure for 7 days or more in temperatures from 50 to 70 degrees Fahrenheit.
- Cure for at least 5 days in hot weather—70 degrees Fahrenheit or higher—or when using high-early-strength concrete.

Applying an Unbonded Topping

The minimum recommended unbonded topping thickness is 3 inches.

The base course should be covered with plastic sheeting or felt that is as wrinkle-free as possible to ensure an unbonded topping. Some contractors maintain that sand over felt helps prevent curling.

Approximately 30 pounds per 100 square feet of wire mesh is needed to control shrinkage cracking. Place the mesh middepth in the topping and cut it at all joints. The maximum aggregate size must be no more than one-third the thickness of the unbonded topping.

Maximum slump should be 1 inch for heavy usage areas.

Joints should be half the topping depth.

Power floating and troweling are usually required, but the final hard troweling should be done by hand.

Correcting Pinholes and Projections

Pinholes and small projections can be corrected as follows:

Cover the concrete with a cement and sand mortar, then rub it over the entire surface with a wood float or medium-grade carborundum stone. A steel float would

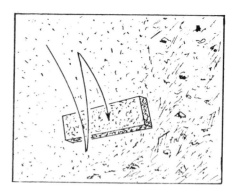

Carborundum stone

Wood float

darken such a surface and make the corrected area obvious.

The mortar is made of 1 part portland cement to 1½ parts concrete sand. For a better appearance, cover a wide area rather than just the defective area. This is similar to grout cleandown, sacking, and rubbing.

Some excellent proprietary cementitious products are available for doing this job with much less labor. Readers should talk to their dealers.

Patching Tieholes

To patch a tiehole, clean the hole, wet it, and apply a neat cement grout of portland cement and water. Then, using a short rod, ram an earth-dry mortar into the hole until the hole is completely filled.

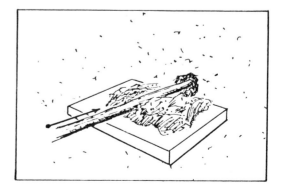

If a form tie wire has been left exposed, the surrounding concrete must be chiseled away so that the wire can be cut far enough down to avoid rust stains.

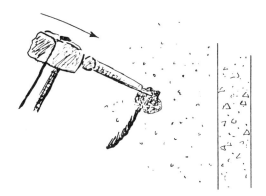

To patch this type of hole, use a mortar that is about the same as that in the original concrete. A concrete of 1 part cement to 2 parts of sand and 4 parts large aggregate takes a mortar patch of 1 part cement to 2 parts sand.

Large patches tend to dry dark, so use a bit of white cement in place of some of the grey—about 20 percent is typical. Experiment with proportions and let the materials dry out for a true comparison. If possible, use concrete sand since it has a range of sand sizes.

Repairing a Broken Corner

A broken corner that is still in good shape can be glued back in place. Clean the area and mix an epoxy. Butter the broken piece with the epoxy, hold or brace it in place for about 10 to 15 minutes, then clean off the excess epoxy.

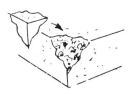

Repairing Honeycomb

Honeycomb repairing is similar to spall patching (see "Patching Spalled Areas" in this book). The honeycombed area should be chipped out and the edges cut away as if for spall patching. Clean and wet the area and brush on a bonding grout containing cement and water, but no sand.

The area is then immediately filled with a mortar of earth-dry consistency. A steel trowel may be used for filling, but a wood float should be used for finishing.

If needed, form a board mark across the completed patch by lining up a board with the existing marks and rubbing it back and forth.

Cure the patch for at least 3 days in temperate weather and longer in cold weather.

For more on concrete repair, see *Concrete Repair: Materials and Methods*, Concrete Construction Publications, Inc., Addison, Illinois, July 1982.

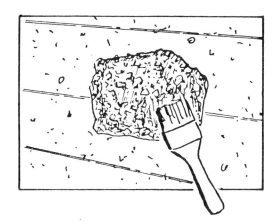

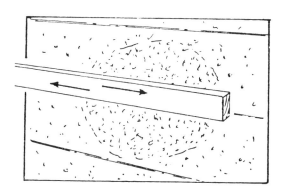

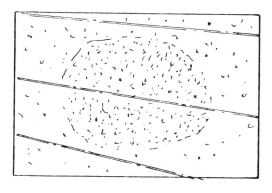

Colored Concrete

Four Ways to Color A Slab

1. **Dry-Shake Method.** Dry-shake is economical and produces bright color because the shake is not overly diluted by surface water.

2. **One-Course Method.** One-course coloring is also called integral color. The concrete is colored all the way through. This method is not widely used except for small areas because of the cost.

3. **Two-Course Monolithic Method.** Colored concrete topping one inch thick is placed on a grey base concrete. The slab is monolithic; that is, the topping is cast so soon after the base slab is cast that the topping and base become one unit. Do not place the topping on bleed water.

4. **Two-Course Bonded Method.** The bonded method is similar to the monolithic method except that the colored topping is bonded to the base slab at some later time. The base course is placed to within 1 inch of grade and the surface left rough for a good bond. The base should be high-quality concrete that is thoroughly cured and kept clean. If a liquid membrane is used for curing the base, it may need to be stripped before the colored topping is applied. Since stripping may be difficult because of the roughened surface, other curing methods are preferred.

After construction activity has slackened—possibly some weeks after the base course is placed—the colored topping is placed. Clean the surface of the base slab first. Thoroughly wet cure the topping.

Making Good Colored Concrete

Use minimal pigment. Generally using less of a strong pigment is better than more of a weak pigment, and using less of a dark color is better than using more of a light color.

White portland cement produces brighter colors, especially when it is used with a light-colored sand. Some authorities recommend white cement even for dark colors.

Keep everything uniform because the only way to maintain uniform color is to make sure that everything going into the concrete and everything done to the concrete is uniform. The materials must be exactly proportioned each time. The color pigment must be the same—if possible it all should be bought at the same time and place. Every batch of concrete should have the same mixing time and the mixer should be kept very clean. The tools must be kept immaculate. The slump should be the same each time—about 4 inches. The subgrade should be uniform in dampness and support. The thickness should be the same. The finishing operations should be identical; extra workers may be needed to assure the same finishing operations each time. Finally, the curing should be the same and should be a type that does not leave streaks.

Cure by ponding. It is probably the best cure for colored concrete because polyethylene cures may cause a greenhouse effect and leave spots or blotches. Whatever cure is used, it should be the same for the entire job to keep the color uniform. A 14-day cure at moderate temperature is recommended. A special wax-cure compound applied by roller is available for colored slabs. It may even be available in the same color as the slab. If a wax-cure compound is used, the surface should also be protected with paper or some other scuff-resistant material.

Use air-entrained concrete to minimize bleeding, which can cause streaking or variations in color. Some color pigments may reduce air-entrainment slightly.

Use of calcium chloride is questionable. Chlorides such as calcium chloride used in cold weather may leave efflorescence on the surface, particularly if more than the recommended amount is used. Other admixtures containing chlorides may also affect the surface. Generally, calcium chloride should not be used for colored concrete.

Use the right type of trowel. Some experts recommend a plastic or stainless-steel trowel for colored concrete.

Regular steel may rub off and leave stains.

Watch for a fast set. Colored concrete may set faster than regular concrete. Troweling too late can discolor the concrete and overtroweling can cause burns.

White Concrete

Cleanliness is most important when working with white concrete. Use special bins to store the cement and aggregate; special equipment for mixing (being especially careful to prevent contamination from iron particles); and clean forming equipment and form release agents. Avoid stains from steel after the concrete is laid.

Mixing, Handling, and Finishing

Waterproofing helps maintain whiteness. If the concrete is to be wet often either from exposure or cleaning, a water-repellent admixture or a waterproof type of white cement is sometimes used to help the concrete retain whiteness.

Water-cement ratio should be low. Use no more than 5 gallons of water per bag of cement (0.44 by weight). Include the moisture content in the sand when calculating water quantity.

Mix proportions are important. For a ⅜-inch topping course for foot traffic only, the recommended mix proportions are 1 part white cement to 2½ parts white sand. Such a thin topping should be placed monolithically; that is, very soon after the base slab is placed so that the two layers become one unit.

Mix proportions for a heavy-duty topping should be 1 part white cement, 1 part white sand, and 1½ to 2 parts of pea gravel or crushed stone graded percentage by weight in the following way:

Passing ½-inch sieve	100%
Passing ⅜-inch sieve	95% to 100%
Passing No. 4 sieve	40% to 60%
Passing No. 8 sieve	0% to 5%

Spread the topping with care because it may discolor if materials in contact with the base concrete are pulled up.

Mechanical floating is preferred, since a stiffer mix can be used.

Dry-Shake Technique

Dry-shake is a method of finishing concrete to change its color or to increase its hardness, wear, or slip resistance. Some dry-shakes can be used to add sparkle or glitter to the concrete surface.

The technique for applying dry-shakes is similar whatever its purpose. Materials are shaked onto the surface and worked into the concrete.

Applying Dry-Shakes

Strike off and bullfloat the base concrete.

Wait until the surface is ready for floating. It should not have any freestanding water and the weight of an adult should make no more than a ¼-inch impression in the concrete. Float the surface by hand or power. Floating helps prepare the surface for the shake by bringing moisture up and removing ridges or depressions. (All tooled edges and joints should be run before and after the dry-shake application.)

Next, spread the premixed shake material by hand evenly over the surface. Use about two-thirds of the material for this operation. Bend low over the slab and let it sift through the fingers. Shake and float the edges first since they tend to set up first. If the shake is applied too early, it will sink into the slab. If it is applied too late, not enough paste remains to finish correctly.

When the shake material is uniformly damp, float it into the surface. A power float is preferred.

Immediately spread the remaining shake material at right angles to the first application.

Then float the surface again after the shake has absorbed moisture.

The concrete may be troweled after the final floating. Flat-trowel first and then use a smaller trowel with an increased angle after the concrete hardens.

Hardness and Wear and Slip Resistance*

Hardness and wear resistance come primarily from the concrete. If the water-cement ratio is low, the mix is right, finishing and curing are done properly—the concrete will be much harder and more wear resistant.

Special aggregates that increase hardness and toughness are available. Special liquid coatings such as epoxies can provide curing, hardening, sealing, chemical resistance, dustproofing, antispalling, and nonslip surfaces.

Wear- and slip-resistant aggregates can be added to the concrete either in special toppings or as dry-shakes. They can provide decorative effects as well. (For placement of special toppings, see the manufacturer's directions and "Resurfacing Slabs" on page 59.)

These shakes can be traprock, granite, quartz, emery, corundum, silicon carbide, aluminum oxide, or malleable iron. These materials are hard and must be worked into the floor with a float and pounded a bit if necessary. They should be worked with a float until they are barely covered with paste. They may need to be dampened and coated with cement before floating them into the surface. The typical ratio by weight for coating with cement is 1 part cement to 2 parts aggregate. Further floating and hard-steel troweling will compact the material into the surface.

---

*For more information on the aggregates and liquid coatings mentioned in this section, check with local distributors and review Division 3 of *Sweet's Catalog File*.

Two popular materials for slip resistance are silicon carbide and aluminum oxide. They are extremely hard and sharp. Finish as if for a color dry-shake and brush with a hair brush several times after the shake is worked into the surface. Allow some time between brushings to make the particles glitter. Use ¼ to ½ pound of shake per square foot.

An iron-aggregate mix or dry-shake should not be applied to a floor if calcium chloride is used, and some silicon-base hardeners may obscure the color.

Exposed-Aggregate Finish by Seeding

For an exposed-aggregate finish to be done by seeding, the base concrete should have a maximum 3-inch slump. Place, strike off, and bullfloat or darby in the usual manner; but keep the level of the surface slightly lower than the top of the forms to accommodate the extra aggregate. The forms should not be too high, however, because the surface must have good drainage when it is washed.

Seed wet, clean aggregate uniformly by shovel and by hand so that the entire surface is completely covered with one layer of stone.

Embed the aggregate initially by tapping with a wood hand float, a straightedge, or a darby.

For final embedding, use a bullfloat or hand float until the appearance of the surface is similar to the surface of a normal slab after floating. Do not overfloat or depress the aggregate too much.

The timing of the aggregate exposure operation is critical. In general, wait until the slab can bear a person's weight on kneeboards without making an indentation. Brush the slab lightly with a stiff nylon-bristle broom to remove excess mortar.

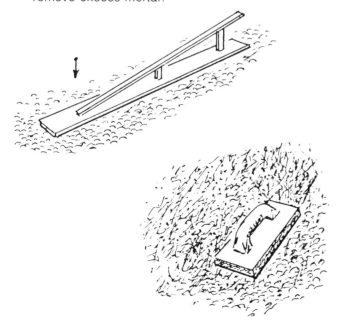

Next, dampen the brush and then brush and flush with water several times. Special exposed-aggregate brooms with water jets are available. If any aggregate is dislodged, delay the operation. Continue until flush water runs clear and no noticeable cement film is left.

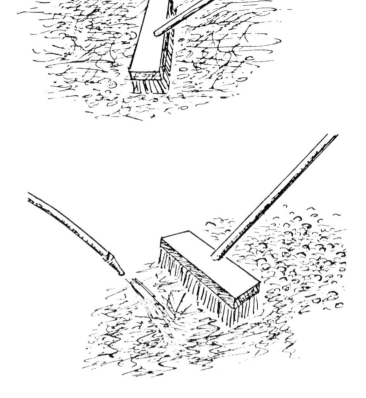

A surface retarder can be sprayed or brushed on the slab shortly after floating to permit a time lapse of several hours before the hosing operation.

Exposing operations should begin as soon as possible after danger of dislodging or overexposing the aggregate is passed. If moving about on the concrete's surface is necessary, use kneeboards. Do not slide or twist the kneeboards; bring them gently into contact with the surface. If possible, stay off the surface entirely to avoid breaking the aggregate bond.

Typically, tooled control joints or edgings are not practical in exposed-aggregate concrete since the aggregate covers the entire surface. Joints can be made by sawing or using permanent strips of wood such as heart redwood.

Exposed-aggregate slabs should be cured thoroughly by using a method that will not stain the surface.

If a sealer is desired, make sure it is compatible with the curing compound.

Wait a few weeks after finishing before applying the sealer. Clean the concrete with an acid wash beforehand if necessary. Remove the acid, dry, and then seal.

Alternate methods for placing exposed aggregate are to use a bonded topping course that contains the special aggregate or to use the integral method in which the select aggregate is contained throughout the full thickness of a slab.

Nonslip Finishes

Floating or troweling is the easiest way to obtain a nonslip surface, but this type of surface may also be the least wear resistant.

The mason can simply eliminate troweling after floating and leave a textured, floated surface, or swirl-float to create a pattern. Similar techniques include the popular broom finish, burlap drag, or wire combing.

Floated Swirl

To produce a swirl texture, the concrete is struck off, bullfloated or darbied, and a hand float is worked flat on the surface in a semicircular or fanlike motion, using pressure. Coarse textures are produced by wood floats and medium textures by aluminum, magnesium, or canvas resin floats. A fine-textured swirl is obtained with a steel trowel. Cork or rubber floats may also be used. Care must be taken to allow the concrete to set sufficiently so that these textures are not marred during curing.

Swirl finish, floated

Burlap Drag

Burlap makes a gritty surface of varying depths similar to a wood float finish. The depth of the finish depends on how soon after the finish the burlap is used. Some burlap has metal projections on the trailing edge to give deeper grooves.

Drag the burlap perpendicular to the flow of traffic.

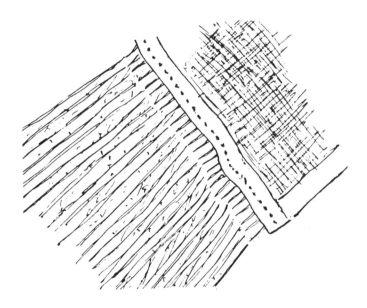

Wire Combing

Wire combing is done with a special tool designed for the purpose. The wire comb should be pulled across the concrete perpendicular to the traffic flow.

Transverse grooving with a steel-pronged rake gives an effect similar to wire combing; however, it requires more skill and is not recommended for large-scale use.

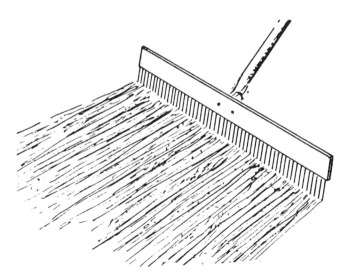

Wire combing

Broom Finish

The broomed texture is very popular. Drag a stiff-bristled broom over the concrete perpendicular to the flow of traffic.

Timing combined with the bristle stiffness and pressure determine the depth of the texture.

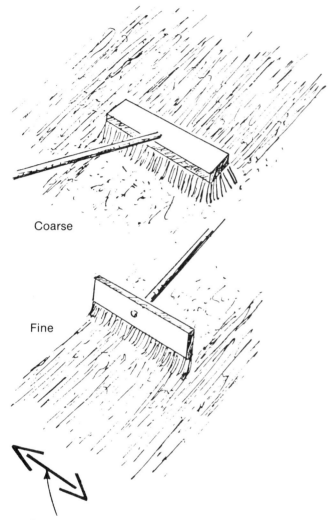

Coarse

Fine

Direction of traffic

Wavy

Other Special Finishes

Rock-Salt Texture

Rock salt is scattered over the surface after hand floating or troweling. The salt is rolled or pressed into the surface so that only the tops of the grains are exposed. After the concrete has hardened, the surface is washed and brushed. This process dislodges and dissolves the salt grains and leaves pits or holes in the surface. The grain size could create holes of about ¼ inch in diameter.

The rock-salt finish is not recommended in areas subject to freezing weather. Water trapped in the recesses of these finishes tends to spall the surface when frozen.

Rock salt texture

Travertine Finish

To attain a travertine finish, apply a dash coat of mortar over freshly leveled concrete. The dash coat should be the consistency of thick paint, and usually contains a yellow pigment. Apply it in a splotchy manner with a dash brush so that ridges and depressions are formed. After the coating hardens a bit, flat trowel to flatten the ridges and spread the mortar. The resulting finish is smooth on the high areas and coarse grained in the depressed areas. It resembles travertine marble. Many interesting variations of this finish are possible, depending on the amount of dash coat, color, and troweling.

Flagstone Pattern

A flagstone pattern is achieved as shown. The joints can be filled with mortar or left open. If they are to be filled, first flood the slab with water to keep it cool and the joints damp. Remove the water. When the surface is free of water, brush in a bonding grout of portland cement and water mixed to the consistency of thick paint. Then pack in the mortar. A sponge and water are useful for cleaning the joint edges. Ideally, two finishers should work together, one painting in the bonding grout ahead of the mortar and cleaning up the joint edges afterward, while the other finisher concentrates on packing in the mortar firmly and neatly.

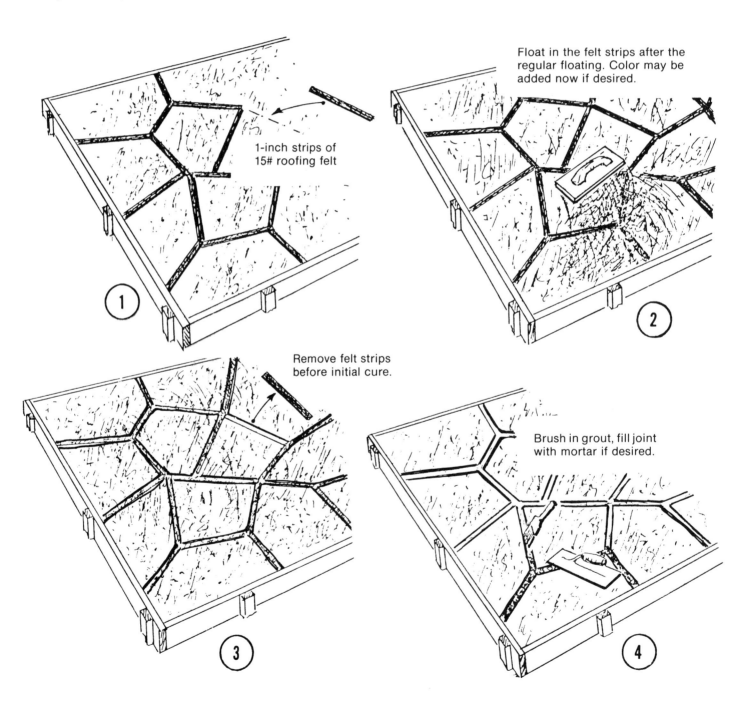

1-inch strips of 15# roofing felt

Float in the felt strips after the regular floating. Color may be added now if desired.

Remove felt strips before initial cure.

Brush in grout, fill joint with mortar if desired.

Flagstone Pattern— Alternative Method

Another way to produce the flagstone pattern is with a piece of ½-inch or ¾-inch copper pipe bent into a flat S-shape. After the concrete has been struck off and bull-floated or darbied and excess moisture has left the surface, the slab is scored in the desired pattern. This tooling must be done while the concrete is still quite plastic because coarse aggregate must be pushed aside as the tool is pressed into the surface.

The first tooling will leave burred edges. After the water sheen has disappeared, the entire area should be floated and the scoring tool run again to smooth the joints. Floating produces a texture that has good skid resistance and is relatively even, but not smooth. This texture is often used as a final finish.

Other Designs

Almost anything may be used to make designs. In addition to the methods shown, pattern stamping can create brick, cobblestone, tile, and many other patterns on concrete.

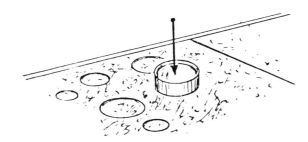
Making circles with a can

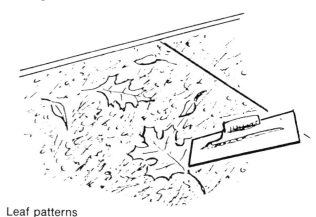
Leaf patterns

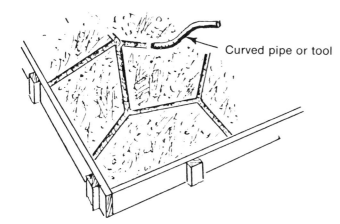
Curved pipe or tool

Appendix
Model Ordinance to Reduce Scaling and Spalling

Homebuilder Bob Schmitt of Strongsville, Ohio, helped draft this ordinance. It is based on his company's practices. The ordinance may not prevent bad practices, he says, but it should "nail down who did it and when," and should "do much to discourage the practices that lead to scaling and spalling."

The ordinance is quite specific about mix design and concrete practices. It requires a written report describing the concrete mix and anything done to the mix. The report must be signed by the supplier, the driver, and the concrete user.

Communities may choose to modify the ordinance to suit local practices. For instance, in areas where freeze-thaw problems do not exist, different mix designs may be specified. Also, curing compound is the only cure listed in the model ordinance. This method is good, but it is not the only acceptable one. Quality control is more important than the type of cure and could be written into the ordinance.

AN ORDINANCE ENACTING NEW CHAPTER___ OF THE CODIFIED ORDINANCES OF THE _(City, Village, Township)___ OF_____ , FOR THE REGULATION OF CONCRETE DRIVE-WAY MATERIALS IN THE _(City, Village, Township)_ OF_____ .

WHEREAS, the presently existing building and construction regulations governing the use of concrete do not adequately protect the residents of the _(City, Village, Township)_ of_____ ;and

WHEREAS, new regulations and standards for concrete construction have been propounded by the Building Officials Conference of North East Ohio and the Building Industry Association of Cleveland with the cooperation and counsel of the Ohio Ready Mix Association and the Portland Cement Association; and

WHEREAS, these regulations propose to protect the residents of a community adopting these standards from defective concrete workmanship and materials:

NOW, THEREFORE, BE IT ORDAINED by the_____ _(Council, etc.)_ of the _(City, Village, Township)_ of_____ , State of_____ :

ARTICLE 1. That the Codified Ordinances of the _(City, Village, Township)_ of_____ be and are hereby amended to include new Chapter __ , regulating the use of concrete in the municipality. The chapter shall include the following sections:

Section .01 Application
This chapter shall be applicable to the construction of any residential driveway and driveway apron, whether or not such construction is intended for public or private use.

Section .02 Concrete Usage; Quality
Any and all concrete used for any of the purposes set forth in Section .01 of this Chapter shall

(a) Contain a cement content of six (6) bags per cubic yard at ninety four pounds (94 lbs) per bag, of Portland cement.

(b) Have an air entrainment of six percent (6%) to eight percent (8%) at the time of pour.

(c) Consist of sound, coarse aggregate of one inch (1") or smaller.

(d) Contain no more water than will permit a slump between a minimum of four inches (4") and a maximum of six inches (6").

(e) Have a uniform thickness of four inches (4").

Section .03 Curing; Mixing; Finishing
(a) Curing compound must be applied immediately after broom finishing, according to manufacturer's recommendation.

(b) Calcium chloride or other admixtures shall not be added at the jobsite.

(c) Minimum floating shall be required. A broom finish shall be required. Finishing must be delayed until water sheen (bleed water) has disappeared from the surface.

Section .04 Base
(a) Base must be smooth and consist of undisturbed or compacted earth. A stone, gravel, limestone screenings, or nonsettling material approved by the building official may be used as a leveling course. Excavations or trenches under a drive must be compacted or filled with a nonsettling material.

(b) Subgrade or base shall be dampened if it becomes dry before pouring.

Section .05 Joints
(a) Control joints, whether hand-tooled or sawn, shall be to a depth of one-quarter the thickness of the slab. The dimension of any control joint panel shall not exceed 10 feet.

(b) Isolation joints shall be required where concrete abuts any structure including, but not limited to, foundations, garage floors, stoops, and paved streets.

Section .06 Time of Pour
(a) If the temperature in the surrounding area is below 70 degrees Fahrenheit, the maximum allowable time from loading to pour shall be 1½ hours.

(b) If the temperature in the surrounding area is above 70 degrees Fahrenheit, the maximum allowable time from loading to pour shall be 1 hour.

ARTICLE 2. That the Codified Ordinances of the _(City, Village, Township)_ of _____ be and hereby are amended to include Section _____ of Chapter _____ for the regulation of concrete plants, suppliers, loaders, contractor, and users, which chapter shall include the following section:

Section .01 Residential Concrete Drive: Plant and Driver's Report

(a) In any construction within the application of Chapter _____, all suppliers shall, at the time of loading for delivery to a user, complete a form titled "Residential Concrete Drive: Plant and Driver's Report, Part 1." This report shall state:

1. Delivery destination
2. Size of load
3. Concrete mix
4. Air entrainment
5. Amount of water added at plant
6. Admixture added
7. Amount of calcium chloride added
8. Time of truck loading

(b) In any construction within the application of Chapter _____, the driver or unloader of the vehicle transporting the concrete used in the construction shall complete a form entitled "Residential Concrete Drive: Plant and Driver's Report, Part II" that shall state:

1. Address or sublot number of pour location
2. Time of arrival
3. Time of pour
4. Name of builder or user
5. Name of cement contractor or user
6. Amount of water added at the jobsite
7. Area temperature at time of pour
8. Curing compound used and type

(c) An original and two copies of the "Residential Concrete Drive: Plant and Driver's Report" shall be signed by the individuals completing the report and the concrete contractor, the contractor's representative, or the user. The above-listed persons do, by affixing their signature to this report, warrant that the statements contained therein are true, under penalty of law. The original shall be sent to the _(Building Department or Official)_ of this municipality, and a copy sent to the builder and a copy retained by the supplier.

ARTICLE 3. Violators of any provision of this Chapter shall be fined not more than $300. Such person, firm, or corporation shall be deemed guilty of a separate offense for each and every violation of a part of any section in this Chapter and shall be fined not more than $300 for each such offense.

ARTICLE 4. That it is found and determined that all formal actions of this _(Council, etc.)_ concerning and relating to the adoption of this ordinance were adopted in an open meting of this _(Council, etc.)_ and that all deliberations of this _(Council, etc.)_ and of any of its committees that resulted in such formal action, were in meetings open to the public in compliance with all legal requirements including Section ___ of the ___(State)___ Revised Code.

WHEREFORE, this ordinance shall be in full force and effect from and immediately after its passage and approval by the Mayor.